PSYCHOLOGICAL TIME
IN
HEALTH AND DISEASE

Publication Number 669
AMERICAN LECTURE SERIES®

A Monograph in
AMERICAN LECTURES IN LIVING CHEMISTRY

Edited by
I. NEWTON KUGELMASS, M·D., Ph.D., Sc.D.
Consultant to the Departments of Health and Hospitals
New York, New York

PSYCHOLOGICAL TIME
IN
HEALTH AND DISEASE

By

JOHN COHEN, M.A., Ph.D.
Professor of Psychology
University of Manchester
Manchester, England

CHARLES C THOMAS • **PUBLISHER**
Springfield • Illinois • U.S.A.

Published and Distributed Throughout the World by

CHARLES C THOMAS • PUBLISHER

BANNERSTONE HOUSE

301-327 East Lawrence Avenue, Springfield, Illinois, U.S.A.

NATCHEZ PLANTATION HOUSE

735 North Atlantic Boulevard, Fort Lauderdale, Florida, U.S.A.

*With THOMAS BOOKS careful attention is given to all details of
manufacturing and design. It is the Publisher's desire to present books
that are satisfactory as to their physical qualities and artistic possibilities
and appropriate for their particular use. THOMAS BOOKS will be true
to those laws of quality that assure a good name and good will.*

Printed in the United States of America

A-2

FOREWORD

Our Living Chemistry Series was conceived by Editor and Publisher to advance the newer knowledge of chemical medicine in the cause of clinical practice. The interdependence of chemistry and medicine is so great that physicians are turning to chemistry, and chemists to medicine, in order to understand the underlying basis of life processes in health and disease. Once chemical truths, proofs and convictions become foundations for clinical phenomena, key hybrid investigators clarify the bewildering panorama of biochemical progress for application in everyday practice, stimulation of experimental research and extension of postgraduate instruction. Each of our monographs thus unravels the chemical mechanisms and clinical management of many diseases that have remained relatively static in the minds of medical men for three thousand years. Our new Series is charged with *nisus élan* of chemical wisdom, supreme in choice of international authors, optimal in standards of chemical scholarship, provocative in imagination for experimental research, comprehensive in discussions of scientific medicine and authoritative in chemical perspective of human disorders.

Dr. John Cohen of Manchester crystallizes the current concepts of the human time sense in response to worldwide awakening of interest in the problem of time—measureless, the immeasurable, the chrysalis of eternity. Time is the most undefinable yet paradoxical of things; the past is gone, the future has not come, and the present becomes the past even while we attempt to define it, and like a flash of lightning, at once exists and expires. Time was, time is, time is past. Let us take time by the forelock to learn from the master the best that has been said and thought about the nature of physical time, mental time, astronomical time, time sense, biological clocks and chemical clocks. Book XI of St. Augustine's *Confessions* reveals the intrinsic nature of the scythe of time which enables us to order our impressions and to time events, but it takes a clock or a procession of calendar units to measure time intervals

v

or orient in local or universal time. Living time sense arises from biological clocks to time reactions to the environment and to stir arthropods into metamorphosis, animals into hibernation, fish into reproduction, birds into molting, animals into migration, plants into flowering. Endogenous clocks are interval timers represented by the breakdown of endocrine products, reactivated periodically by call signals. I heard Albert Einstein remark: "When you sit with a pretty girl for an hour it seems like a minute; but when you are on a 'hot seat' for a minute it feels like an hour. That's relativity." Exogenous clocks include: astronomical clocks constructed from the movements of the earth, moon, sun and stars; Newtonian clocks constructed from changes in electromagnetic and gravitational forces, vibrations of quartz crystals; and chemical clocks constructed from the motions of ammonia or cesium molecules. Psychological time is thus distinct from physical time, its progress recorded in the study of short intervals of subjective time, in the measurement of long intervals of past time, in the mapping of the subjective future to determine the manner in which temporal information is stored in our memories in order to understand its true nature.

Man can create the notion of time by the power of his own mind with millionths of a second and millions of light years as units of physical measurement; animals only have a yesterday, a meaningless tomorrow and an unconceived past and future; and the inanimate have no past, present or future. Man can destroy time by the power of his imagination, for he can speak of the vast passages of history—the remotest past and our future evolution—with the easy confidence of the passing hour. Man's mind has freedom from the temporal sequence, being able to project itself backwards in memory and forwards in imagination. Man's spiritual life is ever an active search; but purpose is meaningless for the finite being without the notion of a future, and therefore of time itself. The sense of time arises from irreversible chemical reactions in accordance with the second law of thermodynamics at a rate regulated by the sun. The linkage of subjective and objective time is thus understood through the participation of man's bodily processes in the irreversibility of Nature and development. A child perceives, judges and conceives time as a relativist, not as an absolutist, paralleling the development of geometrical ideas and growth of speech. A year seems much longer to a child than to an adult; to a 10-year-old, it is a tenth part of his total development and to a 50-year-old, only a fiftieth part. But in each case it is a year in the sense of direction; a year of continued aging in the body and of continued increment of memory in the mind, an inverse relationship pointing to the utility of biological time related linearly to the logarithm of clock time.

Our sense of time arises from internal clock forms which produce repeatable physical phenomena for the nervous system to transmit and register time intelligence. All body structures are under the control of the nervous system; some show rhythmic activity fulfilling the requirements of repetition necessary for a clock form; while others, such as pulse and respiration, emerge from rhythmically acting organs, the heart and lungs. All vital systems exhibit cyclical variations in their activities—daily cycles in hormonal activity, nutrient metabolism, body temperature, blood pressure, blood sugar, electrolyte excretion, wakefulness, sleep, etc.—all linked to natural forces operating in the universe, all behaving as if they were the expression of some property built into the cellular fabric. The body has special "awareness" or subconscious reckoning of molecular activities; and the mind has extreme refinements in measuring the motions of heavenly bodies. The resulting clock mechanisms are so diverse that the concept of time becomes the average of physiological times equivalent to mean psychophysical time. But we rely so much on the sun and watches that we have largely lost this sense of time so highly developed in migrating birds and in sensitive beings. Bergson wrongly contended that subjective time keeps a different rhythm from the planets and the clock. The negative aspect of time (such as death) might cease to oppress us if we could realize human life as a finite pattern in time, capable of all degrees of perfection.

The psychopathology of time embodies the temporal aberrations of patients suffering from brain damage or mental disorder in amnesia, *déja vu* sensation and cyclical variation in symptoms unrecognized as signposts in disease. Time loses its reality in the normal individual with alterations in the rate of thought and feeling in emotional excitement, dreams, hypnosis or under the

influence of drugs. But time is the life of the soul in myth, literature, art and religion. Affective life becomes intelligible in relation
to feelings of time expressed in the profoundest experiences of regret and nostalgia, on the one hand, and of anticipation and hope,
on the other. Forms of experience of time are being correlated to
unravel memory and thought processes and to understand the
theory of perception; and models of subjectivity and objectivity
synthesized from van't Hoff's principle and Arrhenius' equation for
the internal clock become dual pacemakers operating like a film,
exposed at one rate and projected at another. Time thus becomes
a process, a multidimensional, highly variable continuum, with a
relativity no less than space. "We must consider time like space,
as large and free and wide, not as if it were a road, with boards on
either side" for all organic behavior is conditioned by our time
perspectives, each applicable to a different aspect of living, viewing
economic events in one dimension, political in another, social in
another, sexual in another, etc. with no apparent conflict. And we,
with Nature's heart in tune, no longer stand outside Nature like
children with noses pressed against the glass looking in, unable to
enter. We are now looking at time from the inside with the author's
revelations of its infinite movement without one moment of rest.
Nunquam aliud Natura aliud Sapientia dicit.

> *The child lives in the minute*
> *The mealy boy in the day*
> *The instinctive man in the year*
> *The reflective man in the epoch*
> *The true philosopher in Eternity.*

I. NEWTON KUGELMASS, M.D., PH.D., SC.D., *Editor*

PREFACE

N O PROBLEM HAS PROVED more intriguing to thinkers throughout the ages than those posed by the experience of Time. Scientists,
philosophers, theologians and poets, ancient and modern alike,
have all felt the challenge of Time's paradoxes. Sixteen hundred
years ago, St. Augustine, probing his own temporal experience,
unravelled some of the same problems which today engage the
attention of the experimental psychologist. The celebrated passage
in which he describes his bafflement bears repetition:

> For what is time? Who can readily and briefly explain this?
> Who can even in thought comprehend it, so as to utter a word
> about it? But what in discourse do we mention more familiarly
> and knowingly, than time? And, we understand, when we speak
> of it; we understand also, when we hear it spoken of by another.
> What then is time? If no one asks me, I know: if I wish to ex-
> plain it to one that asketh, I know not: yet I say boldly, that I
> know, that if nothing passed away, time past were not; and if
> nothing were coming, a time to come were not; and if nothing
> were, time present were not. Those two times then, past and to
> come, how are they, seeing the past now is not, and that to come
> is not yet?

He goes on to ask: "What do we measure if not time in some
space?" adding: "My soul is on fire to know this most intricate
enigma." Yet such problems were for him not so important as the
overriding question: "How did God spend His time before He
created heaven and earth?" and he was not content to reply, "as
one is said to have done merrily: 'He was preparing Hell for pryers
into mysteries.' "

Among the modern paradoxes which may be cited is one which
the Scandinavian Airlines System, in its brochure on Copenhagen,
sets forth by describing it as a city "which is more than 800 years
old and which grows younger every day." One may wonder at
which point of time in its history Copenhagen began to grow

younger every day. If this reversal of aging began, say, 100 years ago, then the city cannot now be said to be more than 800 years old, unless the assumption is made that it is possible to grow older and younger at the same time. Moreover, how much longer will Copenhagen have to go on growing younger each day before it returns to its starting point? Are we dealing here with a 1600-year cycle, with maxima and minima at alternate 800-year intervals? We must leave these questions to S.A.S.

Voltaire's Zadig has best summed up the paradoxes in his reply to the riddle propounded by the grand magian: "What, of all things in the world, is alike the longest and the shortest, the quickest and the slowest, the most minutely divided and the most widely extended, the most neglected and the most regretted, without which nothing can be done, which devours everything that is little, and confers life on everything that is great?"

Zadig said that it was *time*: "Nothing is longer," added he, "since it is the measure of eternity; nothing is shorter, since it fails to accomplish our projects. There is nothing slower to one who waits, nothing quicker to one who enjoys. It extends to infinity in greatness, it is infinitely divisible in minuteness. All men neglect it, all regret its loss. Nothing is done without it. It buries in oblivion all that is unworthy of being handed down to posterity; and it confers immortality upon all things that are great."

We must realize at the outset that we are dealing here with a profound mystery, in the best sense of this word, which lies at the heart of human experience, on the one hand, and in the "nature of things," on the other. The mystery, such as it is, resides less in the technical difficulty of measurement than in our relationship to events or experiences in so-called past or future time.

And it is not dispelled by the belief, encountered among philosophers, physicists and laymen, that time is an illusion which results from the manner in which our consciousness moves over a fixed sequence, like a policeman's torch over a row of houses on his nightly beat.

The scheme we shall follow begins with distinguishing between the micro- and the macro-structure of temporal experience, in the light of the conception of an internal clock. This will be followed by a discussion of evidence of the relativity of psychological time.

From here we shall move to consider influences on variation in experiences of time, in particular, those encountered in mental disorder and in different social situations. This leads to a wider perspective. From the judgement of duration we move to content and to psychological time as manifested in myth, literature and the history of art. Finally, we make an attempt to sketch a model of subjective time.

ACKNOWLEDGEMENTS

For EXPERT secretarial assistance my warm thanks are due to Miss Nora Williamson, Mrs. Laura Miles and Miss Beulah Morris.

Acknowledgements are also given to the following sources for permission to reproduce their illustrations:

History of Medicine Division, National Library of Medicine (for the portrait of Mach); the *American Scientist* and Professor S. S. Stevens (for Fig. 3, *Three Measures of Apparent Duration);* The Metropolitan Museum of Art, New York, Dick Fund, 1941, (for Daumier's *The Past, the Present, and the Future);* the Journal *of the Warburg Institute* and Professor R. Wittkower (for Reverdy's *Man Prevented by Time from Seizing Chance);* and the Trustees of the National Gallery, London (for Bronzino's *Venus, Cupid, Folly and Time).* I should also like to express my thanks to Mr. Ian Christensen for useful comments on the manuscript in draft, and for compiling the Index, and to Mr. Neil Bolton, a former student of mine, and now lecturer in Psychology at the University of Newcastle-upon-Tyne for help with the survey referred to on page 27.

J.C.

CONTENTS

Page

Foreword v

Preface ix

Acknowledgments xiii

Chapter

1. An Internal Clock 3

2. Micro-structure of Psychological Time 13

3. Past and Future 27

4. Relativity of Psychological Time 40

5. Aberrations of Psychological Time 58

6. Subjective Time in Myth and Literature 72

7. Towards a Model of Psychological Time 83

Bibliography 93

Index 101

PSYCHOLOGICAL TIME
IN
HEALTH AND DISEASE

FRONTISPIECE. Ernst Mach, 1838-1916. Pioneer of the experimental study of psychological time. Reproduced by courtesy of the National Library of Medicine, Bethesda.

Chapter 1

AN INTERNAL CLOCK

I

Every schoolboy knows what it means for time to drag while he is impatiently waiting for a meal. The feeling that his playtime has flown with indecent haste is equally familiar to him, and so is the contrast between the sense of *pastness* attached to his last summer holiday and the sense of *futureness* which colours his next summer holiday. In all these instances, he and we distinguish between time as measured by a clock and time as privately or subjectively experienced. It would seem as though we have another clock within us that may beat more rapidly or more slowly than the outside clock and also—what no outside clock can do—in some sense *retain* past time. Hence our feeling of time dragging or of time flying, of time stored and of time projected, generating impatience or regret, nostalgia or hope.

In 1923, the late Henri Piéron[1] suggested that we could artificially cause our bodily processes to speed up or slow down and thus bring about a corresponding over- or under-estimation of clock time. He had in mind a modification by raising or lowering the temperature of the body, which he assumed would lead to a parallel increase or decrease in the passage of subjective time. His hypothesis was confirmed some four years later by Marcel François,[2] who, in a typical experiment, asked his subjects to tap a key at the rate of three times a second. When he raised their temperature by diathermy, he found that their rate of tapping had increased.

Piéron went on to argue that, just as clock time seems to pass more slowly when temperature is raised, so it would seem to pass more quickly when temperature is lowered. When hot, we would say, "Has an hour not passed *yet?*" and, when cold, "Has an hour gone *already?*"

In the limiting case of deep hypothermia, as reported of men frozen in the snow, both heart and lungs cease to function. Yet this clinical death may be compatible with reanimation, if the cells and tissues have not been irreversibly damaged. On regaining consciousness, the individual would feel that *no* time had elapsed. In the state of *anabiosis* (latent death), the Russian scientist, P. Bakhmetyev, suggested as far back as 1912 that it is as though the pendulum of the internal clock had ceased to swing and only needed a little push to set the clock beating time again.

The general principle relating speed of reaction to changes in temperature had, of course, been established by van't Hoff, and Arrhenius showed that this principle also applied to biological processes. The originality of Piéron's contribution stems from his realisation that subjective time could also be measurably affected.

Further developments came from the work of Hoagland,[3] who was launched on his enquiries by a domestic episode: His wife had developed a temperature of 104°F and asked him to call at the druggist. Although he was away for no more than twenty minutes, she insisted that he was absent for a much longer period. This aroused his suspicion that her "sense of time" had been affected by high temperature. Having checked this hypothesis by a bed-side counting test, his subsequent experiments led him to suggest that the alpha rhythm in man is affected by his temperature and that the chirping of crickets, the heartbeat of cockroaches and similar phenomena in other submamallian organisms vary with changes in the temperature to which they are exposed. He made the supposition that there exist chemical pacemakers in the brain which govern the speed of its metabolism and, through this, the rhythm of subjective time.

Having regard to the small number of subjects involved in the experiments of François and Hoagland, some doubts remain as to the general validity of their conclusions. These doubts have been given substance by recent experiments of C. R. Bell.[4,5] In his first series, he measured the effect of raising the temperature and pulse rate of his subjects on estimations of various intervals of time—45 seconds, 100 seconds, 4 minutes, 9 minutes and 13 minutes. He employed three methods of estimations, *viz.:* (a) counting at an estimated rate of one digit per second; (b) verbal estimation of the duration of a given activity; and (c) production of a time interval designated by the experimenter. The outcome was a negative one in that no systematic relation appeared between the estimates, on the one hand, and the changes in temperature and pulse rate, on the other. The absence of a relationship between changes in pulse rate and apparent duration is in accordance with earlier evidence. However, the failure to demonstrate any effect of increase of oral temperature on apparent duration weakens the François-Hoagland claim.

In Bell's second series, he tried to replicate, as closely as possible, the original experimental conditions of François and Hoagland. The results this time were more favourable though by no means as conclusive as might have been expected. In one of the three tasks assigned to subjects, each subject was required to tap a Morse key at an estimated rate of one tap per second for sixty seconds. There was a significant increase in counting speed (i.e. a decrease in the tapping time) with increase in temperature from $37.21C°$ to $37.72C°$. In the second task, tapping a Morse key at an estimated rate of three taps per second, there was also a significant correlation between increase in body temperature and speed of tapping. In the third task—stopping a variable metronome when it was judged to beat at the rate of four beats per second— the raising of temperature had no effect.

All in all, then, Piéron's original hypothesis still stands in principle. Its universality has still to be established. Furthermore, Hoagland's claim that there is more or less uniformity of response in different subjects is not substantiated in Bell's work. In particular, the apparent discrepancies between the results of different investigators suggest that the concept of a "clock" itself needs modification. Bell's suggestion that a change in body temperature may have a more marked effect on rhythmic than on intellectual activities points perhaps to the possibility that there may be at least two "clocks" operating relatively independently of each other.

II

The issues raised by Piéron's supposition are wider and more complex than may appear at first sight. Since man's earliest history, his patterns of social behaviour have reflected the natural periodicities in his environment: The breeding periods of domesticated animals, seed time and harvest time, seasonal changes in climate, the lunar cycle all became, in one situation or another, social time setters *(Zeitgeber)*. Although man has, by clothing, domestic heating, and food and water storage, become independent of the vagaries of climate, he still remains wedded to the diurnal rhythm of night and day. Heart rate, blood pressure, respiration rate, motor activity, body temperature and urinary flow are synchronized: Peak levels are reached in the day-time, and the lowest levels at night-time. If a change is made in normal sleeping time, physiological processes adjust to the new phase, although some remain unaffected.[6]

Our understanding of human behaviour in relation to temporal phenomena will be seen in better perspective if we assume continuity between man and animal, at least in some aspects of their adaptation to the rhythms of nature. This does not mean that man's sense of time is superior to that of animals, any more than his powers of hearing or smell are supreme in the animal kingdom. It is instructive to learn that the tiny crab *Talitrus* knows the time of day although it has no more than 1 mm of nerve substance.[7] Perhaps if it acquired the habit of wearing a wristwatch, this reliance on an artificial timekeeping aid might dull its natural precision!

A presumption in favour of some internal timekeeping device arises in relation to many biological features apart from changes in temperature. There are, for example, the mass migrations which take place at a certain time of the year. Owls hoot, bats fly, and disease-carrying insects become active at particular times of the day. There is the synchronized flashing of thousands of glow-worms scattered over a wide area, the simultaneous crackling of large numbers of cicadas, and the way thousands of tiny fish, in shoals extending to 15 feet, manoeuver, turn and leap in uncanny temporal unison. These collective responses may be instigated by some visual or auditory signal beyond the reach of the human senses, and there may be some unknown channel of communication whereby a signal is transmitted through the group at such a speed that the result, to the human observer, seems instantaneous.[8]

Behaviour in artificially contrived situations points in the same direction. Experimental animals kept for long periods in continuous darkness display intrinsic physiological rhythms with a periodicity of approximately, but not quite, 24 hours—the so-called *circadian* rhythm. This rhythm is a spatio-temporal pattern of nervous discharge, and it may be activated by cues from within the organism, proprioceptively or centrally, or from outside. Thus a single external signal, provided its intensity is great enough, may initiate a circadian rhythm; a flash of light of 1/2000th of a second can induce a circadian rhythm in *Drosophila* which were previously aperiodic.[9]

A particularly instructive example of the working of an insect's internal clock which may have a bearing on human disease has been identified by Dr. Janet Harker, at the University of Cambridge. Having ingeniously located a 24-hour rhythm in the neurosecretory cells of a cockroach, she exposed cockroaches to two clocks which were out of step with each other. She did this by keeping one group of cockroaches in the light during the night and in the dark during the day, until their clocks were reset, so to speak, to run 12 hours out of phase with those of normal cockroaches, which become active soon after dark. The next step was to implant the neurosecretory cells from the reversed day cockroaches into the normal ones, which were now governed by two clocks set to different times. All the cockroaches developed malignant tumours, mostly in the intestine.[10]

In the last decade or two, there has been a growing interest in the medical implications of internal clocks. Imagine a 25-year-old woman who has suffered from Parkinsonism since an attack of encephalitis in childhood. Each day, however, she enjoys a remission of the disease which lasts two or three hours. Until about 9:00 p.m., she lies in bed entirely rigid except for tremors of arms and legs, and she can neither walk nor feed herself. Her speech and handwriting are unintelligible, and she is euphoric. As 9:00 p.m. approaches, rigidity and tremors vanish, and she eats, speaks, walks and writes normally, the euphoria giving way to apathy. This 24-hour cycle in fact persisted during a 9-year stay in hospital.[11]

C. P. Richter[12] has collected and classified the observed periodicities in a wide range of physical and mental illnesses, including the 24-hour rhythm in the post-encephalitic patient just described. He cites instances of rhythms ranging from 12 hours to 4½ months. A 19-year-old girl, for example, had peaks of temperature for several months at 12-hour intervals, and a 29-year old man developed a duodenal ulcer every 4½ months over a period of 8 years. Other rhythms, in different disabilities, displayed units of 7 days, 9 days, 17-19 days, 24 days or 52 days. One patient had two apparently independent rhythms linked to different days of the week: every Tuesday a swelling in his left knee reached a maximum, while a swelling on his right knee reached a maximum every Friday.

Rhythmic alternations of mood are familiar in everyday life and, to a more marked degree, in psychosis. Circadian and other (e.g., 5-day) mood rhythms are reported in the literature. The regularity, on occasion, has a true clocklike precision: an insurance company official, who had alternate days of depressed and normal behaviour, kept his appointment book with alternate days crossed off his calendar for many months ahead.

The indication that these physical and mental rhythms are endogenous lies in the twofold fact that they are sustained over a long period, sometimes for years, and seem unaffected by variations in temperature, humidity or barometric pressure.

Richter postulates three types of internal clock: peripheral, central and homeostatic, respectively. Peripheral clocks are said to be relatively accurate and are located, he suggests, in the joints, bone marrow or other peripheral zones. Central clocks are probably located in the thalamus, hypothalamus, the reticular formation or posterior lobe of the pituitary. Homeostatic clocks are exemplified by a universal human clock, the female menstrual cycle, which evidently depends on the ovaries, pituitary and hypothalamus.

In a comprehensive review of human circadian rhythms, J. N. Mills[13] has considered a variety of periodicities governed presumably by internal clocks, either wholly or partly endogenous. He discusses the manner in which the circadian rhythm of sleep and wakefulness becomes established in infancy, rhythms in the activity of the adrenal cortex, urinary and hematological rhythms and other periodicities in metabolism, normal and pathological. He draws attention to the practical importance of circadian rhythms in man as indicated by the fact, for example, that mortality from a given dose of a chemical agent seems to be influenced by the time of day at which it is given; a similar variation apparently occurs in post-surgical mortality

He concludes that many human functions are characterized by a circadian rhythm, though this may be subject to exogenous as well as endogenous influences, and he locates the circadian clock tentatively in the hypothalamic region, in view of the evidence of the persistence of temperature and some other rhythms, even in the absence of cortical activity (e.g., in intensive electroshock therapy). Although, he argues, there is no decisive evidence for the existence in man of more than one master clock, it is conceivable that such a clock operates at several different levels of physiological organization. Moreover, many circadian rhythms in man—in EEG, in psychomotor output, in erratic recording of instrument readings and in many occupational activities—all reflect, he suggests, the most basic rhythm of all, namely, sleep-wakefulness, which is enjoyed by Arctic dwellers in the continuous darkness of winter as well as in the continuous daylight of summer.

III

While the physiologist is interested in organic rhythms as such, the psychologist is more concerned with their effects on subjective estimations of the passage of time. It has long been suspected that man has an unknown faculty for judging the passage of time. Under hypnosis, this faculty seems to be exceptionally good, especially in persons capable of swift arithmetical calculation. Indeed, it is the private alarm clock in the form of an ability to awaken at a time decided before going to sleep which has often been invoked as evidence in support of a special sense of time.

This question attracted the interest of early students of hypnosis.[14] Five kinds of suggestion were given in these pioneer investigations: (a) a simple action was suggested during hypnosis to be carried out before the end of the hypnotic trance; (b) the subject was told during hypnosis that the trance would terminate at a specified time; (c) a suggestion was given during hypnosis to the effect that a simple action be performed *after* the trance; (d) a suggestion was given during hypnosis that the subject should awake from natural sleep at a given hour; and (e) the subject was told while awake that he was to pass into the hypnotic state at a specified hour, remain hypnotized for a given period, perform certain actions at prescribed intervals, return to the normal state for a time and finally re-enter the hypnotic condition.

It must be admitted that the claims made by trustworthy observers lend credence to the view that somnambulists possess remarkable non-conscious powers of time-keeping. A somnambulist is unable, after the hypnotic trance comes to an end, to recall what took place. In a typical situation, the suggestion was given to the subject during hypnosis that, at the expiration of, say, 1070 minutes, she was to make a cross on a piece of paper and write down the time she believed it to be without consulting a watch. This instruction was correctly carried out.

A number of different hypotheses have been advanced to account for such phenomena in general and the alarm clock effect in particular. It has been thought, for example: (a) that a person somehow consciously concentrates all night on the moment when he is supposed to wake up (Bernheim); (b) that somnambulists (like dogs and other animals) measure time by "subconscious cerebration" (whatever this may mean), post-hypnotic suggestion being analogous to waking at a pre-appointed hour (Beaunis); (c) that somnambulists are able to "compute" the passage of time in a manner which does not depend on being able to make the necessary calculations, e.g., converting X minutes into Y hours, either in the waking state or under hypnosis (Delboeuf); and (d) that a secondary consciousness watches the passage of time and, when the moment arrives for carrying out a suggestion, takes the place of the ordinary consciousness (Gurney).

These speculations cannot be considered as better than gropings towards a theory. However, the facts claimed to have been established by the hypnotists were supported by a careful experiment conducted, in 1917, by L. D. and E. G. Boring.[15] They studied the accuracy with which the time was judged after varying periods of sleep at night, and the nature and adequacy of the cues for these judgments. They concluded that the time could be judged with fair accuracy, much better than would be expected from mere guessing. Although subjects were told whether their estimates were correct, the estimates did not improve with practice. The estimates were based on various cues, such as degree of fatigue, restlessness, sleepiness, and excretory and digestive sensations. Since the subjects seemed to be fully aware of these cues, no assumption is necessary that the passage of time is judged non-consciously during sleep. This question must, however, be considered within the broader framework provided by the general psychology of time to be discussed in the following chapter.*

REFERENCES

1. PIÉRON, H.: Les problèmes psychophysiologiques de la perception du temps. *Année. Psychol., 24*:1-25, 1923.
2. FRANCOIS, M.: Contribution a l'étude du sens du temps. La température interne comme facteur de variation de l'appréciation subjective des durées. *Année Psycho'., 28*:188-204, 1927; Influence de la température interne sur notre appréciation du temps. *C.R.Soc.Biol. (Paris), 108*:201-203, 1928.
3. HOAGLAND, H.: The physiological control of judgements of duration: Evidence for a chemical clock. *J.Gen.Psychol., 9*:267-287, 1933; Consciousness and the chemistry of time. In Abramson, H.A. (ed.): *Problems of Consciousness.* Josiah Macy, 1951, pp. 164-178.
4. BELL, C.R., and PROVINS, K.A: Relation between physiological responses to environmental heat and time judgements. *J.Exp. Psychol., 66*:572-579, 1963.
5. BELL, C.R: Time estimation and increases in body temperature, *J.Exp.Psychol., 70*:232-234, 1965.
6. Diurnal rhythms in human physiological processes. In *Command 2787,* Report of the Medical Research Council, October 1963, March 1965. London, Her Majesty's Stationery Office, 1965.
7. PORTMANN, A: Preface to a Science of Man. *Diogenes, 40*:3, 1962.
8. HEDIGER, H: *Studies of the Psychology and Behaviour of Animals in Zoos and Circuses* (transl., G. Sircom). London, Butterworth, 1955, p. 64 (also citing Buck, J.B.: *Quart. Rev. Biol., 13,* 1938.)
9. PITTENDRIGH, C.S., and BRUCE, V.G: An oscillator model for biological clocks. In *Rhythmic and Synthetic Processes in Growth.* Princeton, Princeton University Press, 1957, pp. 75-109.

10. HARKER, JANET E: Biological clocks. *Discovery,* April, 1961, pp. 138-142.
11. LEONARD, K: Eigenartige Tagesschwankungen des Zustandbildes bei Parkinsonismus, *Z. Ges. Neurol. Phychiat., 134*:76, 1931.
12. RICHTER, C.P: Biological clocks in medicine and psychiatry: Shock phase hypothesis. *Proc. Nat. Acad. Sci. USA, 46*:1506-1530, 1960. Erasmus Darwin had in 1796 (*Zoonomia,* Section 36) discussed 'The Periods of Disease' in particular solar and lunar influences on biological processes; and Havelock Ellis, in 1931, reviewed the literature on periodicity in disorders of a nervous character (*Studies in the Psychology of Sex,* vol. II, Philadelphia: F.A. Davies, 1931, p. 112).
13. MILLS, J.N.: Human circadian rhythms, *Physiol Rev. 46*:128-171, 1966.
14. BRAMWELL, J. MILNE: *Hypnotism.* London, Thomas Yoseloff, 1960 (first published by Grant Richards, London, 1903.)
15. BORING, LUCY D., and BORING, E.G: Temporal judgements after sleep. In *Studies in Psychology* (Titchener Commemorative Volume). Worcester, Mass., Wilson, 1917, pp. 255-279.

Note to Chapter I. The reference in this chapter to a sense of time in animals raises the question whether a distinction might be made between perceived time or 'perceptual time,' on the one hand, and the idea of time or 'conceptual time,' on the other. We can speak of the 'idea of time' without committing ourselves to any *particular* idea. The expression 'idea of time' may be compared with the expressions 'idea of space' and 'idea of justice.' We can discuss these, or any other, ideas with or without having any specific idea of time, space or justice in mind.

The situation is less simple when we come to interpret 'perceptual time' if, as I assume, all perception is sense perception. For temporal experience is not comparable with visual, auditory, tactile or other sensory experience. There are no special receptors, neural conduction paths or end-stations in the brain for time as there are for vision, hearing, touch or the other senses. In this respect the experience of time has even a weaker claim than the experience of pain to be described as perceptual. At least there are the C-fibres which presumably mediate certain forms of pain, but we know of no fibres which mediate time. Indeed the very notion is meaningless. The words 'perception,' 'perceptual' and 'perceive,' it seems to me, can only be properly employed when there is an awareness which follows a neural excitation which begins at a receptor. This immediately excludes any 'perception' of past or future, because whether I anticipate or reflect on the future or invoke the past is not necessarily dependent on the stimulation of a sense receptor and the passage of a neural impulse along a pathway to the brain; and 'perception' of the present, in the sense of empty or abstract duration, is also ruled out for similar reasons.

Chapter 2

MICRO-STRUCTURE OF
PSYCHOLOGICAL TIME

I

A NUMBER OF REVIEWS[1,2] of the literature on the experience of time have appeared in the past decade or two, the most distinguished being Paul Fraisse's[3] presentation of psychological, in relation to biological, time. Fraisse conceives of three levels of human adaptation to time. The first, which is common to man and animal, relates to rhythms which are set to the periodicities of nature. The second level relates to man's capacity for registering duration and sequence. At the third level, man is in control of time; with the aid of memory, he can now reconstitute the succession of changes that he has experienced and, by anticipation, acquire a perspective for his daily activities.

This view is consistent with the biological orientation sketched in the preceding chapter and allows us to reinterpret studies of subjective time which have been undertaken during the past century. Investigators seem to have been studying properties of a "human clock" without realizing it! Nearly all of our experiences have some duration and occur in a certain order. It is therefore not surprising that among the first questions posed in experimental psychology were those which had to do with judgment of duration and succession. Does the *apparent* duration and sequence of events differ from their *actual* duration and sequence as measured by clock or calendar? The experimental psychology of time begins with an attempt by Ernst Mach[4] in 1860 to measure apparent duration in the sphere of auditory experience.

Mach was particularly interested in the epistemological relation between physics and psychology. Hence his interest in the study of sensation, which he took to be the basic observational datum of all science. The traditional view of the British empirical philosophers (Hobbes, Locke, Berkeley, Hume) had been that the *idea* of succession is generated by the experience of successive sensations. Mach rejected this view and insisted that the idea of succession, like the idea of duration, exists in its own right, on a par with the idea of space. He was thus a Kantian to some extent, in putting time and space on an *a priori* basis.

Mach's enquiries into temporal judgements were inspired by G. T. Fechner's *Elemente der Psychophysik* (1860), and he tried to determine whether Weber's law (later elaborated by Fechner) applied to the estimation of intervals of time. Weber's law may be put as follows: The just noticeable difference of sensation occurs when the stimulus is changed by a certain proportion of itself, that proportion being constant for any given sense. Mach measured the "just noticeable difference," using time intervals ranging from 0.016 to 8.0 seconds. He found that judgments were most accurate at time intervals of about 0.375 seconds, Weber's fraction being about 5 per cent, and he concluded that "the time of the physicist does not coincide with the system of time sensations." He thus succeeded in extending the study of sensations beyond the current interest in their quality, intensity and spatial extensity; the temporal dimension was henceforth included as a legitimate subject of enquiry.

Mach's technique was rather crude by comparison with the "time-sense" apparatus which Meumann devised thirty years later. This equipment consists essentially of an arm rotating around the circumference of a wheel, the arm tripping electrical contacts adjustable on the wheel's rim. The time intervals are defined by the distance between the contacts, and they are recorded on a smoked drum (kymograph), which may also be used to record the subject's responses. Both instrument and drum are driven by an electric motor.[5,6]

Meumann was chiefly interested in differences in the apparent duration of intervals due to variation in the intensities of the sounds or lights which bounded the intervals; differences in judging visual and auditory intervals respectively and differences in judging the duration of filled and empty intervals of time respectively. He claimed: (a) that the greater the intensity of the delimiting stimuli,

FIGURE 1. "Time-sense" apparatus of Meumann (1862-1915).

the more "dense" they seemed to the observer, and this made the intervals of time appear briefer; this effect was less marked as the intervals increased in length. (Other investigators have since shown that if the interval of time is not "empty," but defined by a continuous tone, the more intense sound will seem to last longer. This is possibly an arousal effect.) (b) Meumann also found that the apparent duration of an interval of time delimited by two brief noises is less than that delimited by two visual stimuli, but greater than that delimited by two tactile stimuli; (c) finally he claimed (and most subsequent investigators have accepted this) that if two equal time intervals are compared, the one which is filled seems longer than the one which is empty, but he added that this holds only if the filled interval precedes the empty one.

II

The problem which Mach took up is the one which has perhaps been most intensively examined: what is the size of the brief interval of time which can be judged most accurately? In the typical experiment, the subject is asked to compare one interval with another which is somewhat longer or shorter. The slightest variation in procedure may influence his temporal judgment, which is extremely sensitive to whatever else he is experiencing at the time. Whether the intervals are empty or filled with content seems to matter little so far as fineness of discrimination is concerned. All in all, the evidence seems to point to optimal sensitivity in the "indifference zone"—0.6 to 0.8 second—with over-estimation of shorter intervals and under-estimation of longer ones. In the zone, the differential threshold is about 8 per cent of the interval judged; below or above, it is about 20 or 30 per cent. The zone may correspond to the duration of natural physiological rhythms, such as the heartbeat, or to spontaneous tempo in tapping or walking.[7] It is only fair to point out, however, that others take the view that the "indifference zone" may be nothing more than an experimental artefact.[8]

Recent experiments on other aspects of auditory discrimination have shown that it is much easier for the observer to say that two sounds are separate than to say which one comes first and which comes second. If, for example, two brief and different sounds are separated by an interval as short as two milliseconds the observer can say that there are two sounds; he can *separate* them. But before he can say which sound is first and which is second, that is, before he can place the sounds *in order,* the interval separating them must be between 15 and 20 milliseconds.[9]

Problems of this sort arise in music and speech. In order to be able to perceive a melody, one must not merely be able to discriminate different sound frequencies but also place them in a serial order. The perception of words too, often requires judgment of order as well as of difference (e.g., in distinguishing two very similar words such as *axe* and *ask).* Our auditory is superior to our visual equipment in making fine temporal discriminations, for sounds are, so to speak, strung out in time, while visual displays are spread out in space. And each sense presumably has its distinctive ways of synchronization, retention, recall and what Mme. de Staël called "re-feel."

Instead of asking how brief an interval need be for two signals delimiting it to be felt as distinct, we can turn our attention to the interval itself and ask: what is the minimum perceptible duration between two signals? When both belong to the same sense, this ranges from 50 to 100 milliseconds for vision and from 10 to 20 milliseconds for hearing and for touch. When the excitations relate to *different* senses, the threshold rises from 30-60 milliseconds for hearing and touch to 50-70 milliseconds for vision and touch, and to 80-100 milliseconds for vision and hearing.

Thresholds of separation and order must not be confused with the temporal span of attention.[10] What is the interval of time over which a series of signals may extend and be experienced as unitary? The upper limits are harder to determine than the lower limits because of the ambiguity of the idea of a "unitary" series; at the lower limit the subject has to distinguish the instantaneous from what seems to last for some time. Upper limits ranging from about 2 to as many as 12 or many more seconds have been indicated, and lower limits from 0.01 second for sound to 0.12 second for light."

More recently, attempts have been made to measure the psychological moment in terms of the smallest unit of time which can carry verbal information.[12] If a person listens to a series of words, and the flow of sound is periodically interrupted, the effect of the interruptions on the number of words he recalls depends on the frequency of the interruptions. Almost no information is lost if the rate of interruption is ten per second. It has therefore been argued that under these conditions, a tenth of a second is the irreducible "moment," in the sense that the listener is unable to absorb words in intervals fragmented into smaller units. An alternative method is to measure the duration of an impression in terms of the critical rate at which a sequence of signals is experienced as continuous. Here values of fifteen to twenty per second are indicated (see also Chap. 5).[13]

Whatever the validity of these various thresholds, they do not reveal absolute properties of the external world. Against such an error of judgement Samuel Taylor Coleridge[16] warned us a century and a half ago: "The delicious melodies of Purcell or Cimarosa," he wrote "might be disjointed stammerings to a hearer whose partition of time should be a thousand times subtler than ours," just as "the edge of a razor would become a saw to a finer visual sense." Coleridge seemed not to realize that if our vision were rendered more acute, the dimmest light would seem discontinuous. And if our hearing were more sensitive, we should be disturbed by the collision of molecules in the air; as it is, we respond, at threshold, to movements of the eardrum of less than one per cent of the diameter of a molecule of hydrogen.

It must not be inferred from what I have said that all intervals longer than a few seconds are estimated in the same fashion. There may be a different basis for judging intervals of increasing length— minutes, hours, weeks, months, years, and all these may be subject to characteristic forms of subjective distortion; as we move from shorter to longer intervals, the working of the internal clock becomes more and more obscured by reflective processes.

Some indirect evidence in support of this view, so far as fractions of a second and minutes are concerned, comes from an exploratory experiment at our laboratory conducted by one of my students, L. Bamber. His aim was to measure the relative accuracy with which the following four intervals are judged: 0.25 second; 0.33 second; 1.0 second; and 5.0 second, by three different methods—production, reproduction, and estimation. His apparatus consisted of a circuit linking two Morse keys, two stop clocks and a lamp. In the production method, the subjects had to press a key and thus light the bulb for the appropriate interval. In the reproduction method, this was first done by the experimenter and then repeated by the subject. In the estimation method, the experimenter again produced the intervals which were then verbally estimated by the subject. The four intervals were presented in random order, each interval eight times, in each of the methods. Since the three methods can be arranged in six different orders, he used two subjects (one male and one female) for each order. The most interesting point that emerged was the apparent superiority of the method of reproduction over the other two methods for intervals of one second or less. For the 5-minute interval, the method of estimation gave the most accurate judgements, though with a larger scatter. This seems to bear out the idea that the direct intuition of time is limited to very short intervals, though it seems that William James may have been in error when he asserted that direct intuition is limited to intervals "considerably less than a minute."

Relatively speaking, we are more precise in estimating seconds than minutes or hours, presumably because when the period is brief we can keep our attention bound to the interval itself, but when it is long, our minds wander and our judgements are then more erratic, based, as they are, on such indirect cues as the number and kind of activities that have occupied the time. A break in the stream of consciousness also introduces distortion of temporal judgement, as everyone knows who has fallen into a momentary doze on a journey. The frequency of mind wandering, we have found, varies considerably from one individual to another.[15] The wanderings are recorded in this way: each member of the audience is provided with a bell-push connected with a recording system in an adjoining room. He is told to press it whenever he becomes aware that his attention has *returned* to the lecturer. The bell-pushes are so arranged that when any one of them is pressed, a corresponding torch-bulb lights up in an adjoining room, this being recorded on a moving film. Under such conditions, people press the bell-push, on the average, about four times during a 40-minute lecture, the rate being somewhat higher in a group listening to music. About 3 per cent wander every 2 minutes, and some can sustain an almost unbroken attention. The awareness of normal children seems to return, on the average, about once a minute, the duration of the wanderings ranging from a momentary flicker too short to be timed, to about 4 minutes; the average period of inattention of deaf children, who learn by lip-reading, is about 5 seconds.

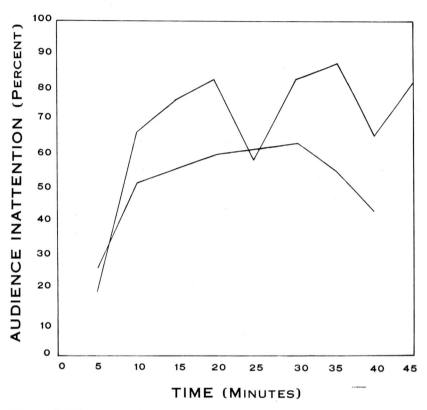

FIGURE 2. Mind-wandering. Per cent of each audience indicating that attention had returned. *Upper curve,* music; *lower curve,* lecture.

TABLE 1

MEAN FREQUENCY WITH WHICH BELL-PUSH WAS PRESSED IN 5-MINUTE
INTERVALS FROM COMMENCEMENT

Interval (minutes)	During Lectures (N = 165)	Listening to Music (N = 33)
5	0.27	0.18
10	0.52	0.67
15	0.56	0.76
20	0.61	0.82
25	0.62	0.58
30	0.64	0.82
35	0.55	0.87
40	0.43	0.65
45	—	0.80

III

Several attempts have been made to set up a psychophysical scale for apparent duration, different investigators employing different ranges of intervals: below one second, 0.25 to 4 seconds; 1 to 20 seconds; and 1 to 60 seconds.[16,17,18,19] The results very much depend on the scaling method used, as may be seen from Figure 3. The top curve is the form that would be expected if the just-noticeable difference were a constant proportion throughout the range, in this instance about 10 per cent. The middle curve is based on mean category judgements made by sixteen subjects on a scale from 1 to 7. The bottom curve is based on the mean judgements of twelve subjects who estimated the duration of an auditory signal. This curve has a slight upward curvature which also appears if the method of fractionation is used, the subjects determining an interval that seems to them half as long as a standard interval.

As S. S. Stevens remarks, it seems that on quantitative (or prothetic) continua, such as apparent duration, the subject cannot equalize the intervals on a category scale because his discriminative ability is not the same at different parts of the scale. Thus, while, for example, he has no difficulty in putting 0.5 second and 1.0 second in different categories, he tends to put 3.5 second and 4.0 second in the same category.

It may be noted that S. S. Stevens has proved himself a persistent critic of Fechner's assumption that the just noticable difference, which is a measure of the variability of a discrimination, is constant throughout the psychological scale. Fechner accepted Weber's law that, at the level of the *stimulus,* the just-noticeable difference is relative to the magnitude of the stimulus; nevertheless he made the assumption that, at the level of the *response,* the just noticeable difference is constant.

No attempt has been made to construct a scale for apparent duration beyond an interval of 60 seconds. In the following chapter, however, evidence is presented which suggests that for intervals up to six months, a scale could be constructed on the assumption of a logarithmic relationship between subjective and chronological intervals.

At this point, we can refer to a seeming paradox in the way we

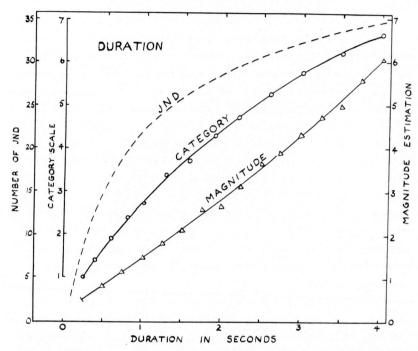

FIGURE 3. Three measures of apparent duration. The *broken-line curve* was obtained by counting off just-noticeable differences. *Circles* mean category judgements by sixteen subjects on a scale. The two terminal stimuli (0.25 and 4.0 sec) were presented at the start to indicate the range, and each observer judged each duration twice on a seven-point scale. *Triangles* refer to mean magnitude estimations by twelve observers (after STEVENS, S. S.: The psychodynamics of sensory function. *American Scientist, 48*(2):226, 1960, with permission of author and editor).

think of subjective and calendar time. It is often remarked that as we grow older the years seem to pass more quickly. What does this mean? As we get older, the metabolic rate slows down, and this presumably has an effect on apparent duration similar to the hypothetical effect of a reduced temperature. That is, calendar time would seem to pass more quickly because subjective time is slower. On this basis, when we look back on the previous subjective year, it will seem to have passed more slowly, in terms of calendar years than the subjective year just completed, for had more subjective units per chronological unit. Or, to put it the other way round, as we grow older, there is a decline in the number of subjective years per calendar year. We do not, however, contradict ourselves when we say that the years pass more quickly as we get older, for then we mean the calendar years seem to pass more quickly, i.e., there are more calendar years per subjective year. To illustrate: suppose a 15-year-old boy is told to tap once per "year." Because he is young and has a relatively high metabolic rate, he will tap say five times per calendar year. Forty years later, when he reaches the age of 55, he will, on the same instructions, tap, say, once in each calendar year.

IV

There is a particular feature of subjective time that enables us to use it as a measure of subjective probability, in the sense of the degree of success we expect to achieve in performance. This feature is the time taken to decide whether to say "Yes" or "No" in reply to the question: "Will you succeed or not?"[20]

A measure of an individual's subjective probability of success (or failure) ψ_S (or ψ_F), in a given task may be obtained by asking him to estimate how many times he would succeed (or fail) in, say, ten attempts at the task.[21] The time he takes to make the estimate may be assumed to vary with his level of subjective probability. The more sure he is of succeeding or failing, the less time he will need to make his estimate. By comparing the times taken to estimate the proportion of successes in ten attempts, at varying levels of subjective difficulty, with the time taken merely to say "Yes" or "No" at the corresponding levels of subjective difficulty, we can obtain Yes-No decision times which may be regarded as indices of subjective probability.

Our subjects consisted of two groups of 12-year-old children ($N_1 = 44$, $N_2 = 32$). Those in the first group merely had to say "Yes" or "No" to indicate whether or not they thought they could hit a ball through a gap. Those in the second group had to say how many times in ten attempts they thought they would succeed in hitting the ball through the gap.

> The subject stood at one end of a table at the other end of which were sliding shutters for presenting gaps of different width. The gap could be varied to introduce a wide range of degrees of difficulty in the task. A screen which could be raised

and lowered in front of the shutters carried a button wired to a concealed chronometer. When raising the screen, the experimenter exposed the gap and at the same time started the chronometer by pressing the button. As soon as the subject announced his estimate or decision the experimenter released the button, thus stopping the chronometer. The interval of time elapsing between pushing and releasing the button was recorded by an assistant who reset the chronometer before each estimate. The subjects had no knowledge that the time they took to make an estimate or decide was being recorded.

We can see from Table 2 that as ψ_s approaches the value 0.5, the time taken to decide "Yes" or "No" doubles from 1 to 2 seconds. On either side of this maximum, the time intervals are symmetrical with respect to deviations of ψ_s from the value of 0.5.

TABLE 2

THE TIME TAKEN TO DECIDE AT VARYING LEVELS OF UNCERTAINTY.

	Difficulty Degree of Subjective	ψ_s	t_s (sec)	$t_{y,n}$ (sec)	H^* (bits)
Hard	0.1	0.0	2.5	0.9	0.00
	0.2	0.1	2.8	1.2	0.47
	0.4	0.2	2.8	1.5	0.72
	0.6	0.3	2.9	1.6	0.88
	0.8	0.4	2.9	1.7	0.97
	1.0	0.5	2.8	2.0	1.00
	1.3	0.6	2.9	1.9	0.97
	1.8	0.7	2.9	1.6	0.88
	2.5	0.8	2.6	1.5	0.72
	3.9	0.9	2.6	1.3	0.47
Easy	8.7	1.0	2.0	1.1	0.00

ψ_s = estimated number of successes in ten attempts expressed as a fraction of unity.
t_s = the time taken to make these estimates.
$t_{y,n}$ = the time taken to say "Yes" or "No" at corresponding levels of subjective difficulty, in reply to the question: "Can you get the ball through the gap?"
$H = - \psi_s (\log \psi_s) - \psi_F (\log \psi_F)$.
*The values in this column are taken from Schmidt.

It is also clear from the table that whatever the subjective probability of success, it always takes less time to say "Yes" or "No" than to make an estimate of the proportion of expected successes. The difference between the time taken to say "Yes" or "No" and the time taken to make an estimate out of ten is smallest at the value 0.5. The difference tends to be greater when ψ_s is low, i.e., when the task sems hard, than when ψ_s is high, i.e., when the task seems easy. We can readily understand why it takes longer to estimate 1 or 2 successes out of 10 than to estimate 8 or 9 successes out of 10, because the possible error involved in making a mistake is much greater relatively in the former than in the latter case.

H.D. Schmidt[22] has remarked on the relationship between "Yes"-"No" decision time, as defined above, and subjective entropy, shown in the final column of Table 2. When subjective uncertainty is at its maximum ($\psi_s = 0.5$), Yes-No decision time is at its longest, and the amount of information transmitted is greatest, falling off symmetrically on either side.

REFERENCES

1. GILLILAND, A. R., HOFELD, J. B., and ECKSTRAND, G: Studies in time perception. *Psychol. Bull., 43*:162-176, 1946.
2. WALLACE, M., and RABIN, A.I: Temporal experience, *Psychol. Bull., 57*:213-236, 1960.
3. FRAISSE, P: *The Psychology of Time* (transl., Jennifer Leith). London, Eyre & Spottiswoode, 1962.
4. MACH, E.: *Contributions to the Analysis of Sensations* (transl. C.M. Williams). Chicago, Open Court Publ. Co., 1897 (first German edition, 1886).
5. BORING, E.G.: *A History of Experimental Psychology*, New York, Appleton-Century-Crofts, 1929.
6. BORING, E.G.: *Sensation and Perception in the History of Experimental Psychology*, New York, Appleton-Century-Crofts, 1942.
7. FRAISSE: *op. cit.*, pp. 116-28.
8. BORING: (1942), p.582.
9. HIRSH, I.J: Auditory perception of temporal order, *J. Acoust. Soc. Amer., 31*:759-767, 1959.
10. See WOODROW, H: Time perception, in Stevens, S.S. (ed.): *Handbook of Experimental Psychology*. New York, Wiley, 1951, pp. 1224-1236.
11. HIRSH, I.J., BILGER, R.C., and DEATHERAGE, B.H.: The effect of auditory and visual background on apparent duration. *Amer. J. Psychol., 69*:561-574, 1956.
12. STROUD, J.M.: The fine structure of psychological time, in Quastler, H. (ed.): *Information Theory in Psychology*, Glencoe, Ill., The Free Press, 1955, pp. 174-205.
13. BRECHER, G.A: Die Entstehung und Biologische Bedeutung der

Subjektiven Zeiteinheit, — des Momentes, *Z Vergleischende Physiologie (Berlin)*, *18*:204-243, 1932-3.

14. COLERIDGE, S.T.: *Biographia Literaria*. London, Dent. 1908, p. 62.

15. COHEN, J., HANSEL, C.E.M., and SYLVESTER, J.D.: *Mind wandering*, *Brit. J. Psychol.*, *47*:61-62, 1956.

16. ROSS, S., and KATCHMAR, L: The construction of a magnitude function for short-time intervals. *Amer. J. Psychol.*, *64*:397-401, 1951.

17. GREGG, L.W: Fractionation of temporal intervals. *J. Exp. Psychol.*, *42*:307-312, 1951.

18. STEVENS, S.S: On the psychophysical law. *Psychol. Rev.*, *64*:153-181, 1957.

19. EKMAN, G. and FRANKENHAEUSER, M: Subjective time scales. *Rep. Psychol., Lab. Univ., Stockholm*, No. *49*, 1957.

20. COHEN, JOHN, HANSEL, C.E.M., and WALKER, D.B.: The time taken to decide as a measure of subjective probability. *Acta Psychol. (Amst.)*, *17*:177-183, 1960.

21. COHEN, JOHN, *Behaviour in Uncertainty*, London, Allen & Unwin, 1964 (New York, Basic Books, 1965).

22. SCHMIDT, H.D., and ZARN, R: Erfolg und Misserfolg als Determinanten einiger Entscheidungsparameter, *Z. Psychol.*, *69*:18-34, 1964.

Chapter 3

PAST AND FUTURE

I

So FAR, WE HAVE been mainly occupied with what may be called the fine grain of subjective time. When we are concerned with the lapse of weeks, months or years, we move to a different order of human time-keeping in which internal clocks can never be more than of minor importance. Although we use the same word "time" to refer both to immediately perceived brief intervals and to long periods that have already elapsed, the mode of estimation may be entirely different in the two situations. We now turn to the study of comparative judgments of long intervals of time, bearing in mind that adult ideas of past and future do not begin in a finished form, like Minerva springing from the head of Jove. They develop, in the light of experience, through the years of infancy, childhood and adolescence. Let us start then with a survey of the stages through which they seem to pass, a survey based on a study of three groups of children, *viz.*:

Age (years)	Number
5 to 7	31
8 to 11	147
12 to 17	163
Total	341

The youngest group were interrogated individually, the two older groups collectively, and they had to write down their replies. They were first questioned about matters which have a temporal reference ("What time do you get up in the morning?" "When do you go to bed?" etc.) as a preparation for the principal question which attempted to elicit from them what they thought were the differences between "past" and "future."

> "You may have heard a person say that something happened in the *past* or will happen in the *future*. For instance, you have had breakfast and we say that it is in the past. But you have not yet had lunch, so we say your lunch is in the future. Again, you have had your Easter holidays, but not yet your summer holidays, so your Easter holidays are in the past and your summer holidays are in the future. Now, what are the differences between *past* and *future?* Think of as many as you can."

With those aged 12 to 17, it was felt to be enough to say: "What are the differences between the *past* and the *future?* List as many differences as you can and place them in order of importance."

Children in the youngest age group who stated a difference indicated, on the average, only one; those in the middle age group gave about 1.5; and those in the oldest group gave about 2.5 differences.

The replies, which were extremely varied, may be conveniently put into five categories, *viz*:

1. Definitions, e.g., the past is before, and the future is after the present; the past has occurred, the future has yet to occur.
2. Reference to a concrete, actual or specific activity, e.g., "You have done (or seen or had) something in the past, you are going to do (or see or have) something in the future."
3. Substantive contrast between past and future, e.g., in terms of standards of living, education, threat of war.
4. Abstract conception of differences, e.g., "We have knowledge of the past but are ignorant of the future;" "The future is uncertain and difficult to predict, whereas the past is certain;" "The future, unlike the past, is new, novelty occurs in the future;" "Mistakes can be made in the future but we cannot make mistakes in the past;" "The past is complete, done with and unalterable;" "We can plan for the future, try to control and change it;" "We look forward to the future and look back on the past;" "We are anxious about the future but not about the past;" "We remember the past and think about it, whereas the future is in our imagination;" "The past is concrete and real but the future is abstract and unreal;" "The past is stationary but we are always moving into the

future;" "The future exerts more influence on the present than the past does;" "The past is a limited period of time, the future is unlimited;" "Things begin in the past and end in the future;" "The future is dependent on the past, but the past is not dependent on the future."

5. No reply, or no adequate reply, including irrelevant remarks, e.g., "The future is a long way off;" value judgments such as: "The future is more important than the past," the difference illustrated by an example: "Here is an example of what the future means. I am going on my holidays in 4 weeks' time."

There is however a relationship between the type of response and the subject's age. Only eight of thirty-one children in the youngest group were prevailed upon to indicate a difference. This took the form either that the past has happened and the future has not happened or that the past is before and the future is after the present.

Sixty-five per cent of the responses given by the children aged 8 to 11 years were to the effect that the past has happened and the future has not happened, and 11 per cent stated that the past is before and the future after the present. Fifteen per cent of the responses given by those aged 12 to 17 years were the same as the most common response of the previous group; 20 per cent referred specifically to material differences; and 14 per cent referred in some sense to knowledge of the past and ignorance of the future.

From this cursory sketch, we can see how rich are the ideas of past and future, even from an early age, as indicated particularly in category 4 above. We wish now to determine whether judgements of different periods of past or future time follow a discernible principle.

II

The capacity to recall events in the order in which they occurred depends to some extent on a particular quality of pastness associated with each separate event. It is this differential quality which may enable us to say how long it seems since this or that event. Estimates of elapsed time may be close to the mark even after two or more days without cues to clock time: two persons placed for 40 and 86 hours respectively in a sound-proof room without temporal cues guessed the time correctly at the end of the period within about half an hour.[1] When longer periods are involved, say, several months, if we may judge from the experience of Michel Siffre, there is considerable under-estimation of the lapse of time.[2]

Siffre is a young French speleologist who spent 63 days alone in a tent set up in a cave 375 feet below the Alpes Maritimes without any outside cue to clock time. A link by telephone with someone at the surface made it possible for a complete record to be kept of the times when he ate, slept and got up, and of his own estimate of the passage of time. The alternation of his periods of activity and rest as well as his digestive and respiratory rhythms turned out to be circadian, about 24½ hours, although his periodic estimates of how much time had elapsed were very gross understatements. He underestimated by almost 50 per cent the length of his working or waking hours. His 7-hour "day" actually lasted 14 hours, 40 minutes. He came out on September 14 believing the date to be August 20. Sixty-three days seemed to him no more than 36 days! This is an effect similar to that due hypothetically to a reduced temperature.

Siffre's underestimation of the calendar time he spent in the cave may be attributable, as his medical examiners suggest, to a form of incipient hibernation which he probably underwent, with a body temperature below 96.8°F. This could cause a slowing down of metabolic processes. If so, Piéron's suggestion would receive some confirmation. Consistent with this explanation is the fact that Siffre displayed a number of disturbed mental features: difficulty in concentration; some amnesia; and a reduced ability to integrate sense perceptions.

This explanation seems all the more credible since the other factors operating were such as might have been expected to produce the reverse effect. Siffre mentions, as being important for him, the uniformity of the environment, the silence and darkness, spatial confinement, isolation and emotional tension. All these ought to lead to a sense of clock time dragging, as in fever. If, in spite of these influences, he still felt the calendar days to be passing swiftly relative to his subjective estimates, we may accept with some confidence the explanation in terms of incipient hibernation and reduced temperature.

Our own approach to the study of the estimation of comparatively long intervals of time has been to employ a method of linear representation.[3] The procedure was as follows: each subject was given a line, say, 10 inches (= 25 cms) long on a sheet of paper and asked to imagine that this line represented his life from birth until now. He was then requested to mark off a length of line representing a given interval since event X. How long does it seem since yesterday's lunch? since last Christmas? since you left school? and so on. A different line was employed for each interval. Seven time intervals varying from group to group were randomly presented to different age groups, 261 subjects in all, ranging from 8 to 75 years of age. In the second and fourth presentations, the endpoints of the line signifying "birth" and "now" were reversed.

In order to clarify this procedure we must distinguish between (a) "How long does it seem since a given event X occurred?" and (b) "At which point on the time scale did the event X occur?" The experiment under consideration relates only to (a). The objective is to measure what might be described as a feeling of "sinceness," a feeling, without conscious calculation, of how long it seems since something happened. This presupposes that the subject does know *when* the something (e.g., last Christmas) happened. If the objective had been to study (b), the subject would have been asked to locate an event on a line regardless of whether he knew *when* the event took place.

It is perhaps also necessary to observe that the use of a linear representation of subjective time should not be taken to mean that this method comes naturally to everyone, as it did, apparently, to Barrow (Newton's teacher) who wrote: "So shall we always represent time by a straight line."[4] While many people spontaneously use spatial images to represent the subjective past and future, by no means all use horizontal lines with the past at the left and the future on the right; some prefer ascending lines and others a closed figure.[5]

III

The chief results may be briefly summarized as follows: The estimates for intervals up to about 6 months from now bear a logarithmic relationship to the length of the corresponding chronological intervals. If we plot the lengths of line marked off against the logarithms of the chronological intervals, we get a straight line. This is in accordance with Weber's law (see p. 14). The logarithmic character of comparative temporal judgements is borne out by another simple experiment. The length of a line drawn to represent a long day is in the same ratio to a line drawn to represent an ordinary day, as the latter is to a line drawn to represent a short day; in these instances the ratio is about 3:2.

Intervals greater than one year from "now" are estimated as if by calculation; there is a linear relationship between the chronological intervals and the length of the line marked off. This same linear relationship appears if we ask the subjects to locate historical events on the line. It seems, accordingly, that by the method of linear representation the subject makes comparative judgements of intervals greater than one year from "now" by locating events. This seems common sense, for the immediately preceding 24 hours, for instance, seem to most people a very long interval by comparison with the preceding month. On the other hand, the previous 5 years seem, on the average, half as long as the previous 10 years. Estimates of intervals greater than one year from "now" can evidently only be made with reference to dates or events in one's personal past to which dates can be assigned.

Estimates of intervals falling between 6 months and one year from "now" are variable. Sometimes they are arrived at as if they belonged to the class of intervals shorter than 6 months and sometimes as if they belonged to the class greater than one year. This variation cannot be put down to scale errors, for it appears in the estimates of groups differing widely in age and for whom the interval of 6 months would therefore be located in a different part of the scale.

IV

The estimates we have been considering in the previous section relate to neutral events in the past which have much the same significance for all members of the groups. We have not been concerned with individual experiences highly charged with emotion. It would appear that our feeling of "temporal distance" from such experiences differs from our feeling of "temporal distance" from neutral events. No experiments, to my knowledge, have been conducted to demonstrate this, and we only have intuition to go by. Leonardo pointed out in his *Notebooks* that "our judgement does not reckon in their exact and proper order things which have come to pass at different periods of time; for many things which happened many years ago will seem nearly related to the present, and many things that are recent will seem ancient, extending back to the far-off period of our youth. And so it is with the eye, with regard to distant things, which when illumined by the sun seem near to the eye, while many things which are near seem far off."

An analogous point was made by Nietszche,[6] although characteristically, perhaps, he refers to a less savoury feature of man, namely, that we never forget anything that caused us hurt or humiliation. Proust hits the same nail on the head, but in Proustian fashion. We believe, he wrote, that we no longer love the dead, but this is only because we do not recall them back to our minds; "if once again we see an old glove, we dissolve in tears, upheld by a flower stalk of remembrance."[7]

If these intuitions are true to life, it follows that our feelings or judgements of "sinceness" would vary with the emotional intensity of what is recalled, rather than with the chronological time that has elapsed since the relevant event.

V

"Futureness" has an overriding significance in human life. A subjective future is presupposed in all our activities. Without a tacit belief in a tomorrow nearly everything we do today would be pointless. Expectation, intention, anticipation, premonition and presentiment—all these have a forward reference in time, the subjective future is that "intimate sense of the distance between desire and the possession of its object." Implicit in all our actions are plans, however vague and inarticulate, for the future, and sometimes, as in saving and investment, this planning is deliberate. Our entire psychic life is permeated with the hope of things to come, the counterpart of nostalgia for the past, but whether, if we had the choice, we should prefer to project ourselves, say, 2000 years into the future or 2000 years into the past, is a moot question, which would be answered differently by different individuals.

Even an animal can grasp something of the future in manner which it is unable to do in relation to the past. It has been remarked that we can indicate to a cat that fish is to be put into its dish but we cannot convey to it that there was fish in the dish yesterday.[8] Nevertheless, only man has an *idea* of the future, just as only man has foreknowledge of his own death.

As we ascend the evolutionary scale, the temporal horizon becomes more and more extended. In experiments on delayed reaction, the interval of delay may be increased at higher phylogenetic levels: the rat can sustain a delay of some 4 minutes, the cat, 17 hours, and the chimpanzee, 48 hours. In man, the horizon may reach far beyond his own brief existence; from infancy onwards there is a growing capacity to relate what is happening at the moment to events foreshadowed in the more and more distant future.

Our orientation to events in the subjective future appears to have the character of a gradient of tension: we become more and more vigilant as an expected event draws near in time. As the ticking of the clock records the passing of the hours and the fateful moment approaches, our hearts beat faster, an experience described in Adelbert von Chamisso's curious tale *The Shadowless Man*.[9]

> Now I remained with my eyes fixed on the hand of the clock, counting the seconds—the minutes—which struck me to the heart like daggers. I started at every sound—at last daylight appeared. The leaden hours passed on—morning—evening—night came. Hope was fast fading away as the hand advanced. It struck eleven—no one appeared—the last minutes—the first and last stroke of the twelfth hour died away. I sank back in my bed in an agony of weeping.

There is a splendid description in Turgenev's *On the Eve* of the agonizing prolongation of time, and then a sudden acceleration, as Elena uncertainly awaits the coming of Insarov. She insists that he must come to see her, at about eleven o'clock the following morning, before his threatened departure. The day then drags slowly, the long, long sleepless night drags more slowly still. Elena gets up and sits stupified in a corner. Nine o'clock strikes: there are still two hours till eleven. She takes up a book, then her sewing, then once again the book. She resolves to walk a hundred times down one of the avenues, and proceeds to do so . . . At last, eleven o'clock strikes. She waits and waits and listens. She can do nothing else but wait; she has even ceased to think. Suddenly her heart comes to life within her and begins to beat ever louder and louder. Oddly enough, the time now begins to pass more rapidly. A quarter of an hour, half an hour, a few minutes more than half an hour go by. Then she starts as the clock strikes not twelve but one o'clock. "He's not coming, he's going away without saying good-bye . . ."

If a sleeper has decided to wake up at a pre-appointed time, he becomes restless as the moment of waking approaches. Every examinee knows this feeling of mounting tension. So does a pregnant woman passively awaiting the birth of her child, a bridegroom the marriage ceremony and a prisoner his execution. Stendhal declared that "the last month is more of a trial than the previous three years. At Melun prison M. d'Hotelans has seen several long-term prisoners die of impatience within a few months of their date of release." We may perhaps assume that, in man, the utility of an ardently desired goal grows exponentially as it is approached in time, until the burden of tension becomes intolerable.

The gradient may be demonstrated experimentally (as well as clinically) in animal and man alike. Pavlov's dogs, conditioned to be fed every 30 minutes, betrayed, by changes in breathing and salivation, that they *knew* when the next meal was due. They could fall asleep in the intervening period and awaken, after signs of restiveness, as the food was about to appear. In man we find that the ability to recall or recognize a task, which has been started but not completed, depends not so much on the amount done as on the amount that remains to be done: the less subjective time needed for completion, the easier the recall of a task, regardless of how much time, within limits, has already been spent on it.[10]

The subjective future, so vital and indispensable a feature of human experience, appears to have no place in the world picture we owe to natural science. Some philosophers assign a lower logical status to the idea of the future than to the idea of the past or present. The past and present, once declared C. D. Broad,[11] are real, but not the future, which is a "non-entity;" so-called judgements about it are therefore not judgements at all, they are neither true nor false. For the psychologist, however, the subjective future may have the same reality as the past or present.

It is possible to obtain some indication of the way we conceive of the future, either in itself or by comparison with the past, by using the same type of linear representation described in relation to the study of the subjective past, though this is not a *measure* in any proper sense. Subjects are presented with a horizontal line of, say, 10 inches, the extreme left of the line being marked "now" and the extreme right, "end of life." They are asked to imagine that this line represents the seeming duration of their future life, and they are asked questions of the type: "How long does it seem to you from now to . . .?" They then mark off a length of line which indicates their answer to the question. In a variation of this method, the *mid-point* of the line is marked "now," the left-hand side of the line referring to the past and extending until "birth," and the right-hand side extending until the "end of life." Some subjects are then asked to mark a point on the line to show how long it seems since their *last* birthday; others mark off a length to show how long it seems to their *next* birthday.

Here are some typical examples illustrating the results, for past and future, obtained from subjects differing widely in age.

a. Eight-year-old children, on the average, mark off a section of 2-inch from "now" on a 10-inch horizontal line to represent a week ago, 3.6 inch to represent the time when Christmas took place, which was 10 weeks previously, and 5.5 inch to represent an event three years previously, i.e., when they had started school.

b. A 13-year-old boy marked off 0.9 inch to represent an interval of one day from "now" (i.e., How long does it seem since yesterday at this time?), 1.8 inch to represent a week from "now," and 8.5 inch to represent 8 years 6 months from "now."

c. A 40-year-old man marked off 0.5 inch to represent 1 day from "now," 0.7 inch to represent 1 week from "now," 3.8 inch to represent 8 years from "now."

d. A 70-year-old lady marked off 0.7 inch to represent a day from "now," 3.7 inch to represent 9 months from "now," 6.9 inch to represent an event 27 years from "now."

The lengths of line marked off for different intervals of future time seem comparable only when they relate to one and the same unit—minutes, hours, days, weeks or years—but when the units differ, a different subjective scale seems to be employed. This is not surprising when we think of the difficulty of translating calendar units to clock units, though both belong to the same dimension.

When the line is marked "now" at its mid-point, a statistical adjustment has to be made to allow for the fact that subjects are not necessarily either at the *objective* or *subjective* mid-point of their lives. If we express median lengths of line representing intervals of 0 to 3 months in the past as *unity,* we find the length for the same interval in the future is about 4. The same ratio of 1:4 also appears in comparing intervals of 3 to 6 months and 6 to 9 months in the past with similar intervals in the future: but a year ahead is represented only slightly, if at all, by a greater length than a year in the past. In so far as we can rely on these results, it would thus seem that we mentally represent future time as a distorted mirror image of the past.

A student of mine, J. J. Foster, conducted an experiment in which he replaced the 10-inch line by a 20-foot line to represent, not the period from birth to the present, but a period of 29 months, this being the interval to graduation day for student subjects concerned (see Table 3). Each subject marked off lengths to represent the following 10 events or points in time:

Tomorrow's lunch
This time next week
Easter vacation (5 weeks ahead)
Examinations at the end of the
    year (15 weeks ahead)
Summer vacation (18 weeks ahead)
Next Christmas (45 weeks ahead)
Summer vacation next year (70
    weeks ahead)
Interim examinations in the third
    year of study (104 weeks ahead)
Final degree examinations (119
    weeks ahead)

The curve is now parabolic, and the data can be represented by an equation of the form $t' = at,^b$ where t' and t are the estimated and actual "times" respectively. If we plot the logarithms of the intervals against the logarithms of the lengths of line marked off, we obtain a straight line.

TABLE 3

LENGTHS FOR DIFFERENT INTERVALS OF FUTURE TIME MARKED OFF
ON A 240-INCH LINE, REPRESENTING TWENTY-NINE MONTHS
(N = 10; each estimate the mean of 4)

Event	Interval of Time to Future Event (Weeks)	Median Length Marked Off (Inches)
1	1/7	4.5
2	1	13.2
3	5	30.3
4	15	53.4
5	18	56.3
6	45	90.0
7	70	134.3
8	104	201·8
9	119	230.0

VI

Our subjective future may also be said to reflect the subjective past when our concern is not limited to empty durations of time. The further ahead we look, the less structured is our vision and the more it is shaped by fantasy, just as a Proustian magic transforms our recollection of the distant past. Indeed, in the limit, there is little difference between our image of the Golden Age in a mythical past and that of a Millenium in an equally mythical future.

Let us ask, in conclusion, whether we should be a happier race of men if, in place of our knowledge of the past and ignorance of the future, we could put knowledge of the future and ignorance of the past.* To this question, first posed by Samuel Butler,[12] we can give the answer suggested by him:

> Sometimes, again, they say that there was a race of men tried upon the earth once, who knew the future better than the past, but they died in a twelvemonth from the misery which their knowledge caused them; and if any were to be born too prescient now, he would be culled out by natural selection, before he had time to transmit so peace-destroying a faculty to his descendants.

REFERENCES

1. MacLeod, R.B., and Roff, M.F: An experiment in temporal disorientation. *Acta Psychol. (Amst.)*, *1*:381-423, 1936.

2. Siffre, Michel: *Beyond Time* (transl., Herma Briffault). London, Chatto & Windus, 1965.

3. Cohen, John, Hansel, C.E.M., and Sylvester, J.D.: An experimental study of comparative judgements of time. *Brit.J. Psychol.*, *55*:108-114, 1954.

4. quoted by Gunn, J. Alexander: *The Problem of Time*. London, Allen & Unwin, 1929, p.56.

5. Guilford, J.P: Spatial symbols in the apprehension of time. *Amer. J.Psychol.*, *37*:420-423, 1926.

6. Nietzsche, F: *The Genealogy of Morals*. London, Foulis, 1910.

7. Proust, M: *Lettres à René Blum, Bernard Grasset, Louis Brun*, p.61. In Poulet, Georges: *Studies in Human Time* (transl., Elliott Coleman). Baltimore, Johns Hopkins Press, 1956, pp. 304-305.

8. Kalmus, H: Communication with animals. *New Scientist*, 11 February, 1963, pp.372-5.

9. von Chamisso, A: *The Marvellous History of the Shadowless Man*. London, Holden & Hardingham, 1913, p.43.

10. Cohen, John: The concept of goal gradients. *J.Gen.Psychol.*, 1953, *49*:303-308.

11. Broad, C.D.: *Scientific Thought*. London, Routledge & Kegan Paul, 1923, p. 66.

12. Butler, Samuel: *The World of the Unborn, Erewhon*. London, Jonathan Cape, 1872, p.191.

Note to Chapter 3. The view of C.D. Broad to which I have referred was expounded by him in 1923 in *Scientific Thoughts*. This superseded an earlier treatment of time by Broad, in 1921. His third and final position is presented in Vol. II, Pt. 1 of Broad's *Examination of McTaggart's Philosophy* (see C.W.K. Mundle, 'Broad's Views about Time' pp. 353-374 in *The Philosophy of C.D. Broad* ed. P.A. Schilpp, New York: Tudor Publ. Co., 1959, Library of Living Philosophers Series).

In his first account of time, Broad took a very different view of the future from that taken in *Scientific Thoughts*. So much so, that he assumed that future events, like past events, must "eternally be." God can therefore have foreknowledge of human actions, although this (Broad held) does not deprive them of free will. In his second account, to which I referred in the text of the above chapter, he maintains that there can be no positive knowledge about the future. Indeed, a statement about the future, at the time it is made, is neither true nor false.

Again, in this second account, the present, having no privileged existence, is no more real than the past, because the only thing that happens to the present when it becomes past is that "fresh slices of existence" have been added to the world's history. The point about an event in the present is not that it precedes an event in the future but that there is nothing which it precedes.

Chapter 4

RELATIVITY OF PSYCHOLOGICAL TIME

I

THE EXPERIMENTAL psychology of time has been, from the start, almost entirely occupied with the measurement of apparent duration as such—that is, with how long an interval seems to be by comparison with what the clock tells us. Such measurements have been made under varying conditions which might be expected to affect apparent duration. Some of these (for example, the effect of the intensity or modality of the delimiting signals) have already been referred to. Psychologists have also been interested, as we have seen, in the study of the subjective order or sequence of signals, by comparison with their physical order, and much effort has been invested in the study of apparent movement, the determination of the conditions under which the subject thinks that he can see an object moving, whereas, in physical fact, no movement takes place. However, only a beginning has been made in the study of the relativity of temporal judgements, which is the principal theme of the present chapter. That relativity characterizes human (and animal) perception in general is well known: we respond not to the absolute magnitudes or intensities or qualities of signals but to relative magnitudes, intensities or qualities; linguistic usage also reflects an analogous relativity.[1,2] We are only now, however, getting to grips with the interdependence of subjective time, distance and speed.

Among the pioneers in this field of enquiry, we must count V. Benussi,[3] whose work inspired a classic experiment by Helson[4,5] which shows the dependence of comparative judgements of distance on the factor of time. Thus, if three points are marked on the forearm, and the interval of time between stimulating the second and third points is greater than that between the first and second, the distance between the second and third points seems to the subject greater than that between the first and second though, in fact, it may be the same or even less. Comparative judgements of tactile distances are thus influenced by the intervals of time which delimit them. This is known as the *tau*-effect. Shortly after Helson's experiment, the same effect was shown to occur if the distances were delimited by visual in place of tactile signals.[6]

More recently, we demonstrated an auditory *tau*-effect by the following experiment. The subject, equipped with headphones, heard three different tones of brief and equal duration. The two successive time intervals (t_1 and t_2), delimited by the three tones, could be varied by the experimenter. Each cycle of three tones was repeated after an interval of 5/3 of the total cycle. The subject was required to adjust the pitch of the second tone until it seemed intermediate in pitch between the first and third tones. Fuller details of the procedure and results are described elsewhere.[7] Here it suffices to point out that when the subject is adjusting the second tone he makes the tones which are presented closer together in time further apart in frequency. For example, when t_1 (the first time interval) = 1 second, and t_2 (the second time interval) = 0.5 second, and the first and third tones are 1000 and 3000 cycles per second respectively, the mean frequency of the middle tone is 1676 cycles per second, by comparison with 1874 cycles per second when $t_2/t_1 = 1$.

A *tau*-movement effect also appears under conditions when subjects walk in one half and run in the other half of their journey: to many of them, the distance seems greater when walking than when running.[8]

II

The converse effect may also be demonstrated, namely, the effect of varying the distance between two signals on comparative judgements of the time intervals separating them. This was first shown to occur in vision under a variety of experimental conditions.[9,10,11,12] Let me describe those studied in our laboratory.[13,14,] Suppose the subject faces a repeated cycle of three flashes of light set horizontally or vertically in front of him, the ratio of the distances between the three flashes varying from 1:10 to 10:1, where the shorter distance is one foot. Each cycle of three flashes is repeated after an interval of 5/3 of the total cycle, which ranges from 0.6 to 6.4 second. The subject can control the timing of the middle flash and he is told to adjust it so that the interval of time between the first and second flash appears to him to be the same as that between the second and third. He thus has to bisect the interval between the first and third flashes.

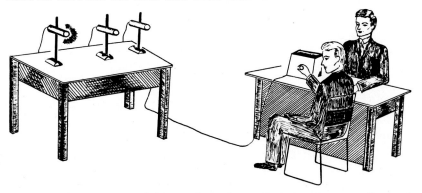

FIGURE 4. *kappa*-effect: Subject adjusts interval of time between first and third flashes.

Under these conditions, the subject allots a shorter interval of time to the greater of the two distances, and the bigger the ratio of the two distances, the greater the difference between the two time intervals allotted to them. Thus, as the ratio of the second distance to the first increases, there is a growing overestimation of the second time interval, as shown in Table 4 and Figure 5.

It is as though the longer distance between the second and third flash *stretches* the subjective time corresponding to it. Hence, if we present two *equal* time intervals, we may infer that the interval of time will seem to last longer which is associated with the greater distance. The magnitude of the observed effect varies with the direction of the flashes of light, being smallest in the upward direction, greatest in the downward and intermediate horizontally.

If we replace the flashes of light by three different tones, we find the same effect, though weaker, possibly because the subject feels that he can safely ignore pitch while he adjusts the middle tone to bisect the cycle of time. A kindred effect may be produced by employing two continuous tones to indicate the intervals of time, instead of three brief tones. The effect of tone on duration is now more marked: the subject allots a shorter duration to the higher

TABLE 4
VISUAL *KAPPA*-EFFECT:
AVERAGE RESULTS FOR 10 SUBJECTS WHEN
$T = (t_1 + t_2) = 1.4$ second.

Ratio of Distances $(d_2/d_1$ in feet$)$	$\dfrac{t'_1 - t'_2}{t'_1} .100$
1/10	-12.1
1/8	-18.8
1/6	-12.1
1/5	-15.4
1/4	-18.7
1/3	-25.8
1/2	- 9.0
1/1	0.0
2/1	15.8
3/1	18.2
4/1	18.2
5/1	25.0
6/1	20.5
8/1	8.2
10/1	13.3

It will be noted in the above table that the total time (T) of the cycle was 1.4 second. Similar results were obtained when $T = 0.6$ second and $T = 6.4$ second. The figures in the second column are adjusted for "time error" effects due to the order of presentation of the two intervals. Each of the ten subjects made four judgements at each distance ratio one pair of judgements with the shorter distance first, one pair with the longer distance first, one of each pair being presented with the right to left direction reversed.

tone than to the lower one, and the greater the difference between the two tones, the more striking is this effect (see Table 5). Thus, apparent duration is demonstrably influenced by auditory as well as by spatial features in the pattern of stimulation. We have called these influences on apparent duration *kappa*-effects.

TABLE 5
AUDITORY *KAPPA*-EFFECT WITH TWO
CONTINUOUS TONES
(AVERAGE RESULTS FOR EIGHT SUBJECTS WHEN
$T = (t_1 + t_2) = 1.5$ second.

First Tone f_1 (cps)	Second Tone f_o (cps)	$\dfrac{t'_1 - t'_2}{t'_1} .100$
3000	1000	-15.5
4000	2000	0.0
2973	2500	- 4.2
2500	2973	7.8
2000	4000	5.6
1000	3000	5.6

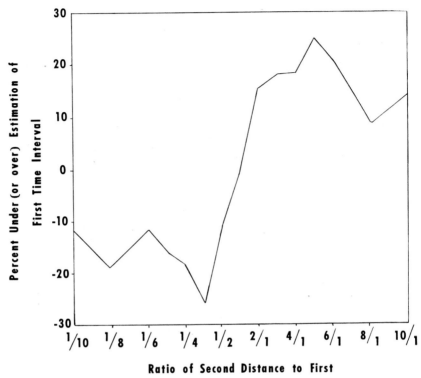

FIGURE 5. Visual *kappa*-effect.

III

We may now ask whether apparent duration is influenced by distance when this is *passively* experienced. This question was first prompted in 1956, when space travel seemed to come within the bounds of the possible, and a dispute took place about its effects on aging. The debate itself was inspired by an inference from relativity theory that if a space traveller moved at a speed close to the speed of light, he would age less rapidly than his friends on earth that he had left behind; one year for him would be equivalent to a decade for them. Let us imagine that the *kappa*-effect holds for journeys in space. A traveller would be subject to acceleration on embarking and to deceleration on landing, and we may suppose that his estimate of the duration of the various parts of his journeys which varied in velocity might be influenced by the corresponding distances through which he had travelled during the respective intervals. The duration of longer distances might seem to him disproportionately great, and the duration of shorter distances disproportionately small, as judged by clocks on the space ship. Similar effects, it could be argued, might appear in a man who flies from London to Paris in an hour and straight away continues his journey from there to Baghdad in another hour; the second lap of his journey might seem to him to last longer than the first.

In the result it was more practicable to come down to earth and study the estimates made by automobile passengers of the duration, distance and speed of their journeys.[15,16,17] Visual cues to distance were excluded either by blacking out the windows of the vehicle or by blindfolding the passengers. The instructions to the passengers were merely that they were to be taken on a journey during which a bell would ring. That was all. The bell was, in fact, rung at halftime. When the journey was over, the passengers estimated the duration and *either* the distance *or* the speed of the two parts of the journey, that is, before the bell rang and after it rang. In Tables 6 and 7 respectively, we show the actual duration, distance and speed of the journeys and the corresponding median estimates. As may be seen from the Tables, nine different journeys were made, ten subjects acting as passengers on each journey.

Analysis of the estimates shows that they are interdependent. If two parts of a journey take the same clock time, that part seems to the passenger to last longer in which the distance and speed are greater. This we call the *kappa*-movement effect.

Under the same conditions, in which the time interval before the

TABLE 6

ACTUAL DURATION, DISTANCE AND SPEED OF JOURNEY

Trial	Before Bell Duration (Min.)	Distance (Miles)	Speed mph	After Bell Duration (Min.)	Distance (Miles)	Speed mph
(i)	10.4	9.3	53.7	8.2	2.3	16.8
(ii)	12.9	8.7	40.5	11.0	2.9	15.8
(iii)	15.3	7.7	30.2	14.6	3.9	16.0
(iv)	14.6	3.9	16.0	15.5	7.7	29.8
(v)	11.1	2.9	15.7	12.1	8.7	43.1
(vi)	8.1	2.3	17.0	11.1	9.3	50.3
(vii)	11.8	5.8	29.5	11.8	5.8	29.5
(viii)	8.0	5.8	43.5	8.0	5.8	43.5
(ix)	6.2	5.8	56.1	6.2	5.8	56.1

TABLE 7

MEDIAN ESTIMATES OF DURATION, DISTANCE AND SPEED SHOWN IN TABLE

Trial	Before Bell			After Bell		
	Duration (Min.)	Distance (Miles)	Speed mph	Duration (Min.)	Distance (Miles)	Speed mph
(i)	15	6	30	14	8	40
(ii)	25	10	40	20	7	40
(iii)	10	5	30	20	8	34
(iv)	15	10	30	28	12	40
(v)	10	5	30	15	6	45
(vi)	15	9	40	20	8	45
(vii)	13	4	28	14	8	33
(viii)	8	4	29	11	8	30
(ix)	9	7	45	8	6	35

bell (t_1) is the same as the time interval after the bell (t_2), we find that the shorter distance, that is, of course, the distance travelled at the slower speed, is overestimated. The longer distance, on the other hand, that is, the distance travelled at the faster speed, is underestimated. From this we may infer that if two parts of *a* journey are of equal *distance* $(d_1 = d_2)$, that part will seem to the passsenger greater which is travelled at the slower speed and for the longer time.

We find, too, under the same conditions $(t_1 = t_2)$, that the slower speed, that is, the speed linked with the shorter of the two distances, is overestimated, and *vice versa,* the longer is underestimated. From this we may infer that if two parts of a journey are travelled at the same *speed* $(v_1 = v_2)$, that part will seem to have been travelled at a faster speed which is associated with the shorter distance and with the shorter time.

The three effects are diagrammatically represented in Figure 6.

It is perhaps necessary, at this stage, to remark that if we express the results of the *tau* and *kappa* experiments in terms of averages, we may obscure the fact that the effects are not invariably displayed by *all* individuals. This is clear in the walking-running experiment in which a number of subjects estimated the *running* distance as greater, although the anti- *tau* effect was less strong that the *tau*-effect. In partial explanation for this state of affairs, we may suppose that those who judge one distance to be greater than another if (other things being equal) it takes more time, may be

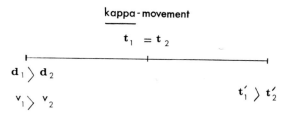

kappa-movement

$t_1 = t_2$

$d_1 \rangle d_2$

$v_1 \rangle v_2$

$t_1' \rangle t_2'$

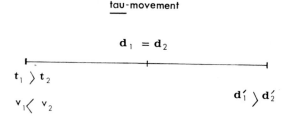

tau-movement

$d_1 = d_2$

$t_1 \rangle t_2$

$v_1 \langle v_2$

$d_1' \rangle d_2'$

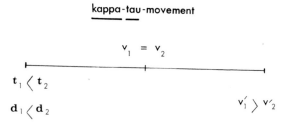

kappa-tau-movement

$v_1 = v_2$

$t_1 \langle t_2$

$d_1 \langle d_2$

$v_1' \rangle v_2'$

FIGURE 6. Diagram illustrating the three subjective movement effects

people who are specially sensitive to the passage of time, as such, while more or less ignoring speed. Those, however, to whom the distance seems *shorter* if it takes more time, may be particularly sensitive to speed: they feel they have covered a shorter distance when walking because they moved more slowly than when running. Such individual differences may conceivably be related to variations in metabolism and tempo, a question which merits further investigation.

What seems clear is that people do not seem able to judge distances independently of the correlative intervals of time. But the influence of time on distance is not necessarily in the same direction for different individuals. Hence, *tau* and *kappa* have to be regarded as statistical effects, unlike illusions to which everyone is subject though not necessarily to the same degree.

IV

We now go on to enquire whether, and to what extent, the estimates of duration, distance and speed are mutually consistent. Are they interrelated in the same way as the interrelations of the corresponding physical variables, time, distance and speed, such that, subjectively, $t' = \frac{d'}{v'}$ $d' = t'$ v' , and $v' = \frac{d'}{t'}$? These relationships might hold irrespective of the way in which the subjects made their estimates. From any two of the three estimates, duration, distance and speed, we can derive the third. This derived value may then be compared with the corresponding direct estimate. For example, we can compare a subject's direct estimate of speed with that which we derive from his estimates of duration and distance. If the interrelations between the subjective estimates were analogous to the interrelations between the physical variables, the differences between direct and derived estimates would tend to zero.

What we find, in the median estimates of duration, distance and speed made by the passengers, is that the estimates are, on the whole, mutually consistent so long as the passenger is travelling at uniform speed. If, however, there is a change of speed, either by acceleration or deceleration, the symmetry in the mutual relationships is disturbed. Passengers then believe that they have been travelling for a longer time than is implied by their combined estimates of distance and speed. Furthermore, their estimates of speed are excessive as judged by their combined estimates of duration and distance, but they *under*estimate distance, as judged by their combined estimates of duration and speed.

It may be noted that the mutual consistency we find at uniform speed is in accordance with the consistency found by J. F. Brown when observers judged the duration, distance and speed of a visibly moving object.

V

A further conclusion, of some practical as well as theoretical interest, is that which relates to passengers' estimates of the speed of their journeys. Under our experimental conditions, the speed of a vehicle is most accurately judged by a passenger at about 30 mph (= 50 kph.). Slower speeds are increasingly overestimated, and higher speeds increasingly underestimated (see Fig. 7).

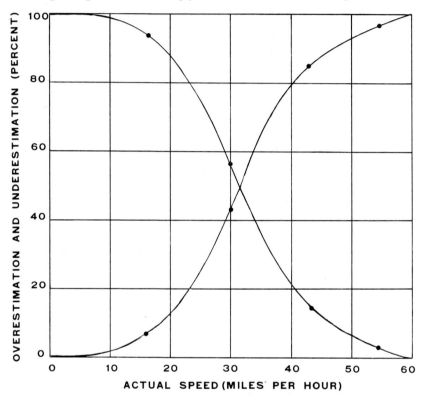

FIGURE 7. Percentage of overestimates and underestimates of speed.

VI

Subsequent experiments, not yet completed, have been concerned with *drivers'* estimates of the duration, distance and speed of their journeys. It is clear that a *kappa*-movement effect seems to characterize the judgements of drivers as well as those of passengers. All our driver subjects were selected for their proficiency in driving, and all prided themselves on being accurate judges of the speed at which they travelled. Yet 40 per cent underestimated their speed when travelling between 48 and 74 mph, with errors ranging from 17 to 100 per cent.

A point of particular interest is the difference between judging duration and distance, on the one hand, and speed, on the other. Neither duration nor distance can be finally assessed until the journey is over. In the case of speed, however, a driver may have it constantly in mind throughout his journey. His estimate is thus not momentary but based on a continuous flow of cues, physiological and psychological, during the journey. A second difference is the apparent possession of an internal "reference" speed by those expert drivers, who did not claim to have a reference duration or reference distance.

In their individual reports, the drivers generally say that they consider both distance and speed when estimating duration, and both duration and speed in estimating distance. In both cases, speed weighs more heavily than the other variable. But in estimating speed, the drivers refer neither to duration nor to distance. Speed is judged by such cues as the noise of the engine, the gear in use, pressure on the accelerator, relation to other vehicles on the motor-way, apart from the "reference" speed.

VII

It would have been more logical to have begun this chapter with a review of the changes in the child's understanding of time, distance and speed and their interrelations, during the years of mental development. Unfortunately, although something is known about the psychogenesis of time, no attempt seems to have been made, apart from the important work of Piaget, to link the child's treatment of time with his treatment of distance or speed, either in perception or in judgement. This is the aim of the present section.

The question we are confronted with, first posed by Einstein to Piaget,[18,19,20] may be phrased as follows: "Is the subjective intuition of time immediate or is it derived?" Piaget was prompted by this question to embark upon a study of the development of the idea of time in young children. The point is this: in classical physics, speed is defined as the ratio of distance to time, which means that distance and time are, so to speak, Newtonian absolutes, primary intuitions, while speed is derived from them. Relativity theory reverses this conception and treats speed as the primary intuition, with time as derived. Einstein evidently wanted to know whether a child first begins to think about time as an absolutist or as a relativist.

The conclusion reached by Piaget is that the primary intuitions of the child relate to speed and distance, the notion of time being gradually disentangled from them. Children, says Piaget, pass through a stage at which they cannot differentiate between temporal and spatial order; "further away in space" signifies for them "more time" because they have not yet grasped the inverse relationship of speed to time. A young child is not able to say how long an interval of time seems to last without being influenced by the correlative distance and speed. Thus, duration is judged on the basis of work accomplished, the distance covered being one aspect of this.

Piaget's conclusion has been challenged by Fraisse,[21] who claims that a child has a primary intuition of time on a par with those of speed and distance, and that time is experienced by a child from the very outset as duration, as an interval between him and the fulfilment of his wishes. Hence a child, according to Fraisse, first conceives of time not as varying inversely to speed but in terms of the effort he expends, and therefore in the light of the changes he subjectively registers.

The point at issue between Piaget and Fraisse reminds us of Mach's critique of Hume and other empiricists. Mach too insisted that the idea of time, like that of space, exists *ab initio* in its own right. Piaget is in the Humeian tradition while Fraisse follows the footsteps of Mach.

From the point of view of *tau-* and *kappa*-effects, we are all relativists, and there is no good reason to exclude children, although little is known of the way these effects are manifested during the years of infancy and childhood. The problem we are faced with, however, is rather different. In *tau-* and *kappa*-situations the subject does not *know* whether the two distances (or the two intervals of time) he is comparing are, in fact, equal or not. If he *knew,* his knowledge would presumably overrule what seems to be the evidence of his senses. In young children, this very often does not happen. Thus, as Piaget remarks, so long as a child is comparing the durations of two objects moving at the same speed, he has little difficulty in saying which object took a longer time. The "trouble" starts when the speeds differ. What is the nature of this "trouble"? The following experimental demonstrations illustrate the problem although they do not finally resolve it.

Two model electric locomotives travel the same distance (16 ft.) on parallel tracks, one moving faster than the other. The slower one (called S) starts earlier and stops later than the faster one (called F). Thus:

At t_0 seconds S starts
At t_5 seconds F starts
At t_{13} seconds F stops
At t_{15} seconds S stops

It is clear that while both locomotives cover the same distance, the slower one must take more time than the faster one. In a variation of these conditions, F moves a shorter distance than S.

The question we put to the children is this: "Which engine takes longer, the slower one (S) or the faster one (F)?" We find that more than a third of children under eight years of age say that the faster one takes longer, in spite of the fact that they can actually see that it starts later and stops earlier. And they give the same reply whether the two distances are the same or whether the slower one travels a longer distance. So far this seems in accordance with Piaget's view that to many children below the age of eight years or thereabouts, "faster" means "more time."

Suppose now that we introduce a change and make the two durations equal by arranging that the slower of the two locomotives travels the shorter distance, as indicated in the following diagram:

Slower
locomotive (S) |————————————|
Faster
locomotive (F) |————————————————|

$$t_S = t_F, \ d_S < d_F$$

Following Piaget's procedure, we ask each child two questions, namely:

1. Which engine stopped first?
2. Which engine took longer?

So far as the first question is concerned, we find that here too our results bear out Piaget's contention that children younger than eight years have no clear notion of simultaneity. Rather more than half say that the faster engine stopped first, and rather less than half that the slower engine stopped first. These proportions remain much the same even at the age of 9+.

When it comes to the second question, we expect, according to Piaget, that children below the age of eight would generally say that the faster engine took longer, because it has covered a greater distance and has "done more work." Yet as many as 60 per cent said that the slower one took longer. And in the age group 8 to 11 years, nearly 90 per cent said so. The large majority of the children who were able to give reasons for their replies stated that the slower one took longer because it was *slower*. A few said that it took longer because there was "less power going to the track" or "because it went a shorter distance," and one said "F was going faster and couldn't take up too much time." Only two children (out of 68) said that "F took longer because it went faster," and only one child said that F took longer because "it covered a longer distance."

Unlike the children studied by Piaget, ours seemed to have less difficulty with this second question than with the first ("Which engine stopped first?"). Indeed, the answers to the two questions were often inconsistent. Thus, only two children aged nine years said that F took longer, but as many as fifteen said that F stopped first!

Accordingly, on two counts our data do not seem to tally with the views of Piaget. For according to him: (a) most children younger than eight years should say that the faster train takes longer; and (b) children above the age of eight years should tend to say that the duration is the same at both speeds. Neither of these expectations is confirmed. We have to conclude that "faster" only means "more work" and therefore more time, when the slower engine moves the same distance as the faster engine or a longer distance. When the slower engine moves a shorter distance in the same time as the faster one, it seems to take *more* time, apparently an anti-*kappa* effect. The very slowness of the engine appears to create an impression of a longer duration; and when the distance of the slower engine is shorter than the distance of the faster engine, there is no longer a tendency to equate faster with "more work" or with "more time."

According to Fraisse, we should apparently expect a judgement of equality at all ages, unless we assume, gratuitously perhaps, that the slower engine seems to the children to exert more effort than the faster one, and also that they identify themselves with the engine.

Piaget's contention that, at least under certain conditions, "faster" to a young child implies "more time" is supported by other data. A child is first asked by Piaget whether, if he runs to school, he goes faster than if he walks. Some children below the age of eight or nine years will say "faster," others will say "slower." Those who reply "faster" are then asked whether this means "more time" or "less time." Piaget declares that "to a large proportion of children between the ages of 4 and 6, and even up to 7 or 8 years, 'faster' means 'more time.' " We have repeated this experiment and find, indeed, that more than half the children under eight years of age who were questioned gave replies similar to Piaget's at Geneva. Some 56 per cent either said that if they run they go faster and this takes more time or that if they run they go slower and this takes less time.

In both of the foregoing experiments with locomotives, the child watches two of them moving simultaneously along parallel tracks and he has to say which one takes more time. He finds the task much more difficult if he observes a single engine moving first at a slow speed and then at a fast speed (or *vice versa*). In a third experiment under these conditions $t_1 = t_2$, and $d_2 < d_1$ $v_2 > v_1$, or *vice versa*. A bell rings at the temporal mid-point of the journey, and the children have to say which part of the journey took longer, before the bell or after the bell.

We find that even up to the age of 11+, children are unable to separate apparent duration either from distance or from speed. Those (mostly under 9 years) who say the faster part of the journey takes longer give, as a reason, the fact that the distance covered is greater, while those (mostly over 9 years) who say the slower part takes longer give, as a reason, the slowness of the engine. Thus there appears to be an age effect with respect to the derivation of duration from distance, on the one hand, or speed, on the other. Those under 9 years of age judge duration by distance; the greater the distance the longer the duration. Children above 9 years of age judge duration by speed; the slower the speed the shorter the duration. Only one of our subjects, an 11-year-old, said, "I think they were the *same* times, because the train was going slower when it had less distance to cover and faster when (it had) more distance to cover."

Thus here too it turns out that Piaget's account seems to require some modification. While those under nine years of age reply in accordance with Piaget's thesis, those above this age run counter to it in one respect. That is, while they do base their judgements of duration on their impressions of speed, they do not say that the engine moving at the faster speed takes more time. Thus, a comparative judgement of *successive* durations, made by children above the age of 9 years, follows the same pattern as a comparative judgement of *simultaneous* durations when the slower engine moves a shorter distance.

The evidence so far points to the primacy of speed over duration. Further evidence may be adduced from an experimental situation in which the distances covered by the two engines are the same but the durations and speeds are different ($d_1 = d_2$, but $t_1 > t_2$ and $v_1 < v_2$, or *vice versa*). Here it seems that children above the age of 9 years tend to justify their statements that one distance is greater than another on the ground that it was covered at a greater speed, not because it took more time. Thus the two speeds are perceived as different, and this distorts the comparative judgement of distances. The perception of a difference in speed is not compensated for by a perception, in the opposite direction, of a difference in the two durations.

The logical difficulties experienced by the young child of 6 or 7 years of age are to a large extent due to his inability to coordinate the different perspectives offered by considering the situation simultaneously, from the standpoint of time, distance and speed. This difficulty is brought out in a conversation on time I had with a bright 5-year-old boy. He told me first that it is always *yesterday*. Why? "Because today we call yesterday 'yesterday,' tomorrow we shall call today 'yesterday,' and the day afterwards we shall call tomorrow 'yesterday.' " A little later he said,

"No, it is always tomorrow." Why? "Because yesterday we called today 'tomorrow,' and today we call tomorrow 'tomorrow,' and tomorrow we shall call the next day 'tomorrow.' " Some minutes later he revised his position and said, "No, it is always today." Why? "Because yesterday we said it was 'today.' Today we say it is 'today,' and when it is tomorrow we shall say 'today.' "

After he had passed his sixth birthday I raised the same question and he replied, "Sometimes it is yesterday, sometimes it is today, and sometimes it is tomorrow." He was still unable to see that a day could be all three, depending on the point of view.

The conclusion we are led to is that in spite of the revision that seems necessary in Piaget's explanation, his reply to Einstein's question is borne out by our experiments with young children and is consistent too with the results of our experiments with adult drivers.*

Perhaps this conclusion does no more than echo the sentiments expressed by Lucretius[22] 2000 years ago:

> Time also exists not by itself, but simply from the things which happen the sense apprehends what has been done in time past, as well as what is present and what is to follow after. And we must admit that no one feels time by itself abstracted from the motion and calm rest of things.

REFERENCES

1. COHEN, JOHN: *Chance, Skill and Luck,* Harmondsworth, Pelican Books, 1960, see Chapter 9.
2. COHEN, JOHN, DEARNALEY, E.J., and HANSEL, C.E.M: A quantitative study of meaning. *Brit.J.Educ. Psychol., 28*:141-148, 1958, Pt. II.
3. BENUSSI, V: *Psychologie der Zeitauffassung.* Heidelberg, Carl Winter's Universitätsbuchhandlung, 1913.
4. HELSON, H: The *tau*-effect—An example of psychological relativity. *Science, 71*:536-537, 1930.
5. HELSON, H., and KING, S.M: The *tau*-effect—An example of psychological relativity. *J.Exp.Psychol., 14*:202-217, 1931.

---

*NOTE: The experiments with the drivers on the road described in Section VII and with the children (described in Section VII), were conducted with the help of Mr. Akio Ono and Mr. Brent Skelly, both Research Assistants in the Department of Psychology at the University of Manchester.

6. GELDREICH, E.W.: A lecture room demonstration of the visual *tau* effect. *Amer.J.Psychol., 46*:483, 1934.

7. COHEN, JOHN, HANSEL, C.E.M., and SYLVESTER, J.D: Interdependence of temporal and auditory judgements. *Nature, 174*:642, 1954.

8. COHEN, JOHN, COOPER, P., and ONO, AKIO: The hare and the tortoise: A study of the *tau*-effect in walking and running. *Acta Psychol. (Amst.), 21*:387-393, 1963.

9. ABE, S: Experimental study on the correlation between time and space. *Tohoku Psychologia Folia, 3*:53-68, 1935.

10. ABBE, M: The spatial effect upon the perception of time. *Jap.J. Exp.Psychol., 3*:1-52, 1936.

11. ABBE, M: The spatial effect upon the perception of time : Simultaneous comparison of phenomenal size of two time intervals divided by three stimuli. *Jap.J.Exp.Psychol., 4*:1-12, 1937.

12. ABBE, M: The temporal effect upon the perception of space. *Jap. J.Exp.Psychol., 4*:83-93, 1937.

13. COHEN, JOHN, HANSEL, C.E.M., and SYLVESTER, J.D: A new phenomenon in the judgement of time. *Nature, 172*:901, 1953.

14. COHEN, JOHN, HANSEL, C.E.M., and SYLVESTER, J.D.: Interdependence in judgements of space, time and movement. *Acta Psychol. (Amst.), 11*:360-372, 1955.

15. COHEN, JOHN, and COOPER, P: New phenomena in apparent duration, distance and speed. *Nature, 196*:1233-1234, 1962.

16. COHEN, JOHN, and COOPER, P: Durée, longueur et vitesse apparentes d'un voyage. *L' Année Psychol.*, No. 1, 13-28, 1963.

17. COHEN, JOHN: Psychological time. *Sci. Amer.*, 1964, November, pp. 116-124.

18. PIAGET, J: *Le développement de la notion de temps chez l'enfant.* Paris, Presses Universitairies de France, 1946.

19. PIAGET, J: The development of time concepts in the child. In Hoch, Paul H., and Zubin, J. (eds.): *Psychopathology of Childhood.* London, Grune & Stratton, 1955, pp. 34-44.

20. PIAGET, J: *Psychology and Philosophy.* In Wolman, B. J., and Nagel, E. (eds.): *Scientific Psychology.* New York, Basic Books, 1965, pp. 28-43.

21. FRAISSE, P: *The Psychology of Time* (transl., Jennifer Leith). New York, Harper & Row, 1963, pp. 262-280.

22. LUCRETIUS: *De Natura Rerum* (transl., H.A.J. Munro). London, Bell, 1914.

Chapter 5

ABERRATIONS OF PSYCHOLOGICAL TIME

I

LIKE MECHANICAL CHRONOMETERS, our internal clocks are subject to their own characteristic disorders. In the ordinary course of daily life, our impression of the sequence of two events does not depart wildly from the actual and, indeed, we need to be able to recall experiences in a sequence corresponding, roughly, at least, to the order in which they happened. Nevertheless, discrepancies do occur. Mach[1] noted that if a doctor concentrates his gaze on the patient's blood, he may see it squirting out before the lancet has entered the skin, even if there is one sixth of a second in favour of the lancet. Generally speaking, if we attend to the second of two signals occurring in rapid succession we can subjectively reverse the physical time order. Furthermore, the feebler of two stimuli presented at the same moment is usually perceived later than the other. The explanation for both phenomena, Mach suggested, lies in the fact that we can only attend to one thing at a time; we have the greatest difficulty in attending equally to two signals presented simultaneously, even in the same sense modality; and if the signals are simultaneously presented to two *different* senses, they never seem to occur at the same moment.

We serve as somewhat peculiar clocks, not only by a special play of attention but also when directly comparing an interval that is passing with one that has elapsed. For example, a subject is instructed to read aloud, at a rate of what he believes to be one per second, a series of digits presented in random order. He is then asked to estimate the duration of the elapsed reading period. Under these conditions, the quotient "past time"/"present time" proves to be less than unity, where "present time" is measured by the number of digits read and "past time" is a retrospective estimate of this period. The quotient declines with increase in the length of the interval during which the digits are read aloud, and it reaches a stable level at intervals of about 20 seconds. The investigator has interpreted this to mean that the amount of time retained is less than the amount perceived. There is some difficulty, however, in understanding precisely what the quotient means, since the numerator and denominator are expressed in different units. Moreover, the notion of "amount of time retained" requires further clarification (see Chap. 7).[2]

II

We move towards larger discrepancies between private time and clock time (a) in mental illness, including states of heightened emotion, (b) under hypnosis and (c) under the influence of drugs. Let us consider these in turn, with the reminder that we have already touched upon the way subjective duration may be affected by changes in temperature.

In normal life we need to sustain many of our memories, which are potential recollections, a perpetuation within us of representations of our past experience. At the same time, there is a ceaseless interplay between the representations of the past and the uninterrupted flow of information from the external world. Just as, according to the resonance theory of Claparède,[3] our past may be at the service of the present, so the present may be remotely controlled by our past: in the words of Shelley in *Adonais*: "Swift as a Thought by the snake Memory stung." In mental disorder, the normal reciprocal relations between past and present are accentuated and caricatured: the meaning of the present becomes the puppet of the remote, childhood past, while the past itself may be inaccessible because it is repressed or distorted out of all resemblance to reality.

The ability to recall past events in their true order is an essential element in the sense of personal identity, and it is disturbed in Korsakow's syndrome and in early senile dementia. In paresis, a patient may believe that he has remained the same age since his illness began. Furthermore, in the state of depersonalization, time, as it were, seems to stand still; the immediate past may seem to the patient exceedingly distant, while current events seem merely to repeat once again what has already happened. Similar effects occur in extreme fatigue and in *déjà vu* and remind us of those psychotics who are sure, after five minutes, that they have been kept waiting for six months. In states of aggressive depression, calendar time is equated by the patient with unending time, or particular intervals of time are grossly distorted. A patient says, "I am Adam, the first human being, who cannot die." Another declares, "My mother has to live for 2,000 years in torment and torture." A third asserts that he has destroyed the world from the beginning and will continue to destroy it into eternity.[4] Some light is possibly thrown on these subjective transformations of time if they are regarded as mechanisms of defence which enable the patient to face up to his situation; withdrawal from the hard facts of life is translated into a remoteness of the world itself and into a cessation of time.[5]

Patients suffering from an amnesic gap sometimes feel that the clock or calendar is very slow and sometimes that it is very fast. Thus, one patient who had lost his memory for a period of eight months felt that the gap between his last recollection before the amnesia and his first recollection after it, was no more than one night. Another patient whose gap covered a period of two days felt the time that had elapsed between the two recollections was very much longer.

Comparable disturbances of temporal judgements are said to occur in diffuse organic disease of the nervous system, in typhoid and in cerebral deterioration linked with alcoholism. But these reports are commonly nothing more than clinical descriptions of individual patients. Thus, sometimes the effect described may simply be due to high temperature which makes the hours seem to fly: "Very often he said at two o'clock that it was five." Sometimes the aberration may not be strictly a temporal one, but delusional in a broader sense, as when a patient who had been in hospital a few weeks believed he had been there for seventeen years.

A peculiar type of temporal derangement is encountered in those obsessives who cannot bear time's unalterable flow and behave as if in fact they could reverse it, as in *déjà vu*. Some would like to do away with time, like Rousseau, who threw away his watch and thanked heaven that it would no longer be necessary for him to know the time of day. Had he been a citizen of Samuel Butler's *Erewhon,* where anyone owning a watch is liable to imprisonment, he would have felt completely free from anxiety.

Not far removed from such persons are the patients whom Ernest Jones[6] has described as suffering from a so-called "God-complex," marked by a feeling of omnipotence in relation to time. *Their* time is valuable by comparison with that of others; *their* time is correct, and they alone are justified in being unpunctual. *Their* recollection of past events is the only true one, just as *their* prediction of future events will alone be fulfilled.

A particular form of disturbance is temporal claustrophobia.[7] The patient fears that he lacks time or has no time; he feels enclosed and imprisoned by his tasks and obligations. This encapsulation in a cage of time can be as disturbing as spatial claustrophobia. There also seems to be a temporal counterpart to agoraphobia in those persons who are in dread of the "expanse of time." They rush from one activity to another in an effort to fill up their time, the emptiness of which corresponds to empty spaces for the agoraphobic. It has been suggested that these phobias are symptomatic of a regression to a childhood and that they represent a state of anxiety unconsciously induced by a forbidden temptation which the conscious fear is designed to conceal. Empty time may, on this view, unconsciously signify the opportunity for masturbation or erotic adventures. A frantic filling up of time serves as a defence against such fears. "Claustrophobias in time" may signify a loss of the power of voluntary decision-making.

The problem of subjective time confronts us dramatically in epilepsy, and an understanding of what occurs in this nervous disorder may throw some light on the entire subject. That time in the form of some minimal duration is required for consciousness is a penetrating observation first made by Hughlings Jackson[8] with reference to epilepsy: for the loss of consciousness which takes place in an epileptic seizure is due, he suggested, to the sheer rapidity of neural discharge: "During the *excessive and rapid discharge* of the anatomical substrata of consciousness, we could not expect that conscious states would appear; on the contrary, we should, *a priori,* expect loss of consciousness." Perhaps the same is true of the timelessness of sexual ecstasy, which a modern poet has described as "Time's emergency."

Here an analogy suggests itself between abnormal functioning of the brain and the sharp discrepancy which might appear between the rate at which a camera takes films and the rate at which they are projected. The conventional rate of presentation of frames in sound films and television is 24 per second, silent film requiring no more than 16-18 frames per second. If it is intended to show a film in slow motion, it is usual to take 64 frames per second (the presentation rate naturally remaining at 24). In scientific films, where great detail may be required, a high-speed camera may take between 5000 and 10000 frames per second.

If our visual system did not act as a kind of protecting buffer to the brain by regulating the rate of information transmitted to it, the effect of a sufficiently large number of frames per second on the viewer might, presumably, be comparable to that of an epileptic seizure. The experience would be "timeless," because of the rapidity of neural discharge, and the viewer would lose consciousness. This does not, in fact, happen, because our eyes (and other senses) regulate the rate of input of information. Under mescaline and similar drugs, however, as we shall see, the visual system is bypassed, and inner experience seems greatly speeded up even to the point of obliterating consciousness.

The minimal duration of a visual experience, or the psychological "moment," may be defined in terms of the rate at which the successive presentation of static images is seen as apparent movement *(phi*-phenomenon). A flowing sequence of images is experienced if frames are presented at, say, 16-18 per second, each frame lasting 60-70 milliseconds. Tonal sensation, too, begins when the number of cycles per second is of this order of frequency; and eighteen tactile signals per second is the point which divides a clearly differentiated series of tactile impressions from an impression of tactile vibration. It has accordingly been suggested that the psychological moment may be regarded as an interval of about 0.06-0.07 seconds, which corresponds to a rhythm of about 16-18 "beats" per second. The rhythm can be accelerated by stimulants and slowed down by sedatives. The "moment," as thus defined, would have a different duration for different species. For instance, the "moment" of the snail, which registers fewer impressions than man per unit of time, is said to be about 0.25 second, while that of a fighting fish, which registers more impressions, is about 0.03 second.[9]

III

It is possible to induce deliberately a distortion of temporal judgement in a hypnotized individual.[10] He is told, for example, that he will be given, say, 10-minutes to perform a given task, the actual time being only 10-seconds. Yet he is afterwards certain that he has been active for 10 minutes. There are good reasons for accepting that such individuals are telling the truth, that is, that they really believe they experienced an interval of 10 minutes. The most convincing reason is their ability to build in time signals given by the experimenter. Usually, the signal is woven into the fabric of the subject's story in much the same way as we assimilate into our dreams signals which impinge upon our senses during sleep. But the hypnotized subjects demonstrate extraordinary precision in reporting the signal as having been received at the appropriate moment in subjective time. If the actual time is 10 seconds, the hypnotic time 10 minutes, and the signal is given after 2 seconds, the subject, on awakening, reports that he received the signal about two minutes after entering the trance. Such temporal distortion is no more mysterious than other phenomena of hypnosis. It reveals that the hypnotist is able to make his subject accept beliefs uncritically, even if they are at variance with objective circumstances.

It is hardly necessary to add that a hypnotized person does not really have the capacity for cramming 10 minutes work into 10 seconds. Otherwise, Tristram Shandy, who, when engaged in writing his autobiography, was distressed by the thought that it took him 2 years to describe all the details of the first 2 days of his life, might have sought reassurance from a hypnotist. Bertrand Russell has argued that Tristram Shandy was unnecessarily perturbed, and that even if he had been immortal, so long as he did not get tired or bored, he could easily have completed his entire biography. It is hard to see the force of this argument, and some philosophers have been quick to remark that if Russsell himself attempted to write his biography as fully as Tristram Shandy did, he would soon find a growing discrepancy between the time it took him to describe his experiences and the (much greater) time taken to enjoy them.[11]

The special effect of somnambulism and hypnotism on the awareness of the passage of clock time must be distinguished from the alleged "timelessness" of the Freudian "unconscious." "It is constantly being borne in upon me," wrote Freud,[12] "that we have made far too little use in our theory of the indubitable fact that the repressed remains unaltered by the passage of time—this seems to offer us the possibility of an approach to some really profound truths. But I myself have made no further progress here." Elsewhere[13] he declares that the Kantian notion of space and time are necessary modes of thought and may be re-examined in the light of psycho-analysis. He repeats the claim that "unconscious mental processes" are "timeless," not arranged chronologically; time alters nothing in them, nor can the idea of time be applied to them. It cannot be said that other analysts have made much progress, although Marie Bonaparte[14] has attempted to dissect the concept of "timelessness." She casts doubt on the suggestion that "repressed psychic content" remains unaltered by time, whatever we may think consciously. But her evidence is essentially intuitive, and her contention that "the unconscious has no knowledge of time" is hardly more helpful than her assertion that "the unconscious does not perceive time."

IV

Under the influence of mescaline, hashish and *cannabis indica* and drugs of similar pharmacological structure, the effect we have seen to occur in fever is greatly enhanced. De Quincey tells us that after taking opium, one night might seem to him "of a duration far beyond the limits of any human experience." One of my own subjects under mescaline, like others described in the literature, stated that his "sense of continuous time was lost." The interval which seems endless while it lasts may, retrospectively, seem considerably contracted. Such experiences occur not only in terrestrial fever, but also in heavenly trance, at least for the faithful follower of Mahomet. "For such a one," wrote Gibbon, "a moment of pleasure will be prolonged to a thousand years, and his faculties will be increased a hundred fold to render him worthy of his felicity." And what felicity! The Koran promises, for the meanest of believers, seventy-two *houris* of resplendent beauty, in blooming youth, of virgin purity and exquisite sensibility.

Walter de la Mare[15] has given us a first-rate description of the effect of mescaline on his friend, J. Redwood Anderson. Mr. Anderson felt his thoughts to be much accelerated, but his own movements—possibly because he *saw* them—as well as the events in the vicinity, seemed to him much retarded. To the onlooker, however, Mr. Anderson's *actual* movements were feverishly quick. When he got up from a chair to open the door, he seemed to the observer to be moving at a rapid speed, but he himself, by the time he had got to the middle of the room, felt that it was ages since he had risen from his seat and he could hardly recall what he had intended to do. These effects have often been corroborated by other observers. Thus, a patient of Schilder's remarked; "You glance at your watch and the second-hand creeps at an unobservable snail's pace . . . No matter how many steps I took, the hill in front came no closer. I was doomed to walk forever in this valley, never approaching my destination, never getting further from the place I had left behind."[16]

Returning to Mr. Anderson, it is worth noting that he was able to judge the passage of time with fair precision. He seemed to see an enormous tape-measure, calibrated in seconds, minutes and days. A pointer moved along the scale, and when he was asked to tell the time, all that he had to do was to look at the pointer: the scale seemed to him as real as the ground under his feet.

If the effect of mescaline (and allied drugs) resembles, in some respects, the effect of an epileptic seizure, we must suppose that in the former, as in the latter, the rate of neural discharge is considerably accelerated, although not so much under mescaline as in epilepsy. Hence, while consciousness remains, time seems inordinately stretched out.

Aberrations of spatial impressions tend to accompany distortion of temporal experience under mescaline. The subject of mine, to whom I referred earlier, reported that his "self" seemed utterly remote in space, while time seemed to him to stand still. This space-time kinship has been observed in other instances. One of Bromberg's[17] patients declared: "When I walked it was as if somebody was holding me back . . . I did not gain. I felt as if I walked very slowly."

Finally, even a cursory review of the psychopathology of time would be incomplete without a reference to so-called experimental neurosis which may be induced by imposing temporal demands greater than the organism can bear. If Pavlov's dog was fed every half hour, and one meal was missed, the dog's salivary secretion would begin to flow two or three minutes before or after the half hour had elapsed. But if the animal was given a readiness signal, by sounding a metronome thirty seconds before the half hour had elapsed, its "sense of time" became sharper, and secretion would not begin if the metronome were sounded a minute or more too soon. H. S. Liddell[18] has found similar effects in sheep and goats, and he has established that it is the readiness signal which proves the last straw. A sheep in a Pavlov frame which is given an electric shock every six minutes becomes restless two or three minutes beforehand. But a ten-second readiness signal given before the six minutes, proves too much for the poor sheep. The signal compels it to develop a keener sense of time, but presently the stress becomes too great, and the animal's behaviour is totally disrupted. Although these experiments have not shed much light on the human experience of time, it is possible that a knowledge of the reactions of animals under conditions of temporal constraint may shed light on human disorders in the time-bound cultures of our day.

V

Apart from the sheer aberrations and vagaries of man's internal clock, there is another source of variation in our judgement of time. This is the value placed upon it. Some people cherish their time and dispense moments with studied parsimony. Others thoroughly enjoy wasting their own time and, into the bargain, take a special delight in dissipating other people's time. Subjective time for these latter may be symbolic, in that its value is displaced from some source of which they are unaware. Theorists of the psycho-analytic school have suggested that the tendency to hoard time is a legacy of the anal phase of childhood, just as the dissipation of time may signify a genital delight in promiscuity, but it is hard to verify or falsify such interesting speculations.

An individual who values his time wants to be in control of it, and this may influence his choice of a vocation. There are people who find it intolerable to be paced by a clock, that is, to begin and stop work at a precise moment which they themselves are in no position to choose. They prefer to be bound to a task. And there are differences in the extent to which temporal precision is demanded from different occupational groups. It seems that, in general, the higher the status of a post, the less punctual one can allow oneself to be. In the British Civil Service, it was once possible to identify the grade of an official by the time of his arrival at work.

In industrially developed societies, time is the most precious asset because it makes possible the production or provision of all goods and services. Hence it is redeemed by ceaseless activity, and it is calibrated in economic units: Time, we say, is money. We measure output per unit of time. Interest on money invested grows in time. Above all, a Puritan ethic urges us not to waste time in pseudoactivities.

This explains the difficulty many people feel in accepting the idea of free, leisure time, in which a person can do what he likes, for free time is the antithesis of time treated as the basic value in economic production. Time-saving devices are our symbol of industrial efficiency, the quality of a device being measured by its speed. The precious time saved must not be frittered away in frivolous pursuits. When George Bernard Shaw was told that a certain athlete had broken a world record by running a race in one tenth of a second less than the champion, he asked: "What will the new champion do with the time he has saved?"

It is well known that varying systems of time calibration are to be found among peoples at different levels of cultural development. Simple agricultural or pastoral societies punctuate the passage of time by regularly recurring tasks of social significance, such as watering, milking the cows or home-coming of cattle. Moreover, each tribe may have its own system of calibrating time. The Aranda of Western Australia divide the day into twenty-five parts. The Tumerehà Indians reckon the year as 10 months, apart from 2 further months during which the year is dead. The Cree Indians ignore the days when they are unable to see the moon. Among the Trobriand Islanders, past events, real and mythical alike, are included in a universal present, or in a different kind of time, but not in a previous phase of present time. In the Luapula Valley, the passage of time has a twofold meaning, depending on whether it is linked with a definite personal history or with universal history, and there are variations from one personal history to another. The history of any sub-clan is self-contained and cannot be compared with the history of any other sub-clan; all periods are defined in terms of the events which occurred in them.

Modern societies need a more precise and reliable measure than can be given by recurring social events or by bodily rhythms, such as the growth of hair or nails. They need a calendar subdivided into equal units, regardless of social or private rhythms or events.

But there is no absolute significance in the conventional division of time employed by modern societies. Nor is there anything absolute in the value they place upon time. Valuation of time reflects socio-economic pressures to which people are subject and their habits of zestful industriousness. In places where indolence has long been the rule, it is hard to arouse a sense of urgency in workers or induce them to work at speed. "There is not an inhabitant in this island," wrote a Governor of Ceylon, "that would not sit down and starve out the year under the shade of two or three coconut trees rather than increase his income and his comforts by his manual labour." This was in 1802, and there are still vast areas in Africa and Asia where no value is placed, as it is in the West, on doing something quickly for its own sake. I have myself found, in the Middle East, that it is virtually impossible to get schoolchildren to do psychological tests of any kind which depend on speed. Where a Western child naturally gets down to the task as quickly as possible, the Middle Eastern child appears to have little feeling for speed as such. He gives the impression that he has all the time in the world to do what is required of him. This is, of course, a purely cultural effect.

The Calvinist injunction that time is money will no doubt continue in force in factories and offices where employees are paid for the time they devote to the job. Outside the factory, however, this rule is being reversed to read: "Money is time." The worker becomes better placed to bid against his employer for his own time. The more money he makes per hour, the more free time he can afford to take. N. N. Foote has pointed out that once a consumer gets beyond the point at which his chief concern is survival, it is not the capacity to purchase objects which counts most for him, but the purchase of time. One use of this new free time is to provide an opportunity for do-it-yourself activities. In doing something for himself, the consumer does not simply calculate the cost of a home decorator against his own pay. What he values is the interest of the task.

The value which people place on their time was dramatically displayed in 1752 when the English finally accepted the Gregorian calendar, already adopted by other European countries in 1582. To compensate for the inadequacies of the Julian calendar, the 3rd September, 1752 was reckoned as the 14th, with widespread rioting as a consequence: the people clamoured: "Give us back our eleven days!" Even now, many adolescents believe that when the clock is moved an hour back in winter or forward in summer, they get younger or older respectively.

We may conclude with the common observation that many people, as a matter of habit, keep their watches, say, half an hour fast, knowing full well that this is so. They are not deceived by their own self-deception! Yet this arrangement is important for them and they feel uncomfortable, as though they had suddenly been closely cropped, if their watches are put to run accurately. The fact that the watch is fast gives them a margin of safety, as it were, an insurance against being late. The custom of a friend illustrates this tendency rather precisely. Whenever he travels from Manchester to London, he moves the hands of his watch forward eight minutes just as he reaches London Airport. He says that this device is to ensure that he arrives promptly at meetings. Traffic congestion and greater distances in London add more uncertainties to the journey. It is as though our friend allows himself, at Manchester, a certain level of risk (or subjective probability) in keeping an appointment. Let us assume that he usually thinks that there is a chance of 0.7 that he will arrive on time. In order to maintain this level of subjective probability he advances his clock by eight minutes. He seems to prefer to do this rather than embark on each journey eight minutes earlier—the average additional journey time.

REFERENCES

1. MACH, E: *Contributions to the Analysis of Sensations* (trans., C. M. Williams). Chicago, Open Court Publ. Co., 1897 (first German edition, 1886).

2. FRANKENHAEUSER, M: *Estimation of Time*. Stockholm, Almquist & Wiksell, 1959.

3. CLAPARÈDE, E: La genèse de l'hypothèse. *Arch. de Psychol., 24*: 1-55, 1933.

4. SCHILDER, P: The psychopathology of time. *J. Nerv. Ment. Dis., 33*:530-546, 1936.

5. SCHILDER: *loc. cit.*

6. JONES, E: *Essays in Applied Psycho-Analysis*. London, Hogarth Press, 1951, pp. 257-259.

7. FENICHEL, O: *The Psycho-Analytical Theory of the Neuroses,* New York: Holt, 1943, p. 296.

8. JACKSON, HUGHLINGS: In Taylor, J. (ed.): Selected Writings. London, Staples Press, 1960, Vol. I.

9. PORTMANN, ADOLF: Time in the life of the organism. *Man and Time, Papers from the Eranos Yearbooks*. London, Routledge, 1958, pp. 310-11; see also Brecher, G.A: "Die Entstehung und biologische Bedeutung der subjektiven Zeiteinheit,-des Momentes," *Zeitschrift für vergleichende Physiologie* (Berlin), *XVIII* (1932-33), pp. 204-243.

10. COOPER, L.F, *et al.*: *Time Distortion in Hypnosis*. Baltimore, Williams & Wilkins, 1959, Second edition.

11. e.g., GUNN, J. ALEXANDER: *The Problem of Time*. London, Allen & Unwin, 1929.

12. FREUD, S: *New Introductory Lectures on Psycho-Analysis*. New York, Norton, 1933, p. 105.

13. FREUD, S: *Beyond the Pleasure Principle* (trans., Hubback, C.J. M.): London, Hogarth Press, 1942, p. 32.

14. BONAPARTE, MARIE: Time and the unconscious. *Int. J. Psychoanal., 21*:427-468, 1940; see also Meyerhoff, H.: *Time in Literature*. Berkeley and Los Angeles, University of California Press, 1955, pp. 153-154.

15. DE LA MARE, WALTER: *Desert Islands.* London, Faber & Faber, 1932, pp. 91-96.
16. SCHILDER: *loc. cit.*
17. BROMBERG, A: Marihuana intoxication. *Amer.J. Psychiat., 91*:303-330, 1934.
18. See Liddell, H.S: *Emotional Hazards in Animals and Man.* Springfield, Thomas, 1959; and also *Discussions on Child Development,* Tanner, J.M., and Inhelder, B. (eds.): London, Tavistock Publications, 1956, p. 144, Vol. 2.
19. MEYERHOFF, H: *Time in Literature.* Berkeley & Los Angeles, University of California Press, 1955.
20. COHEN, JOHN: The scientific revolution and leisure. *Nature, 198*: 1028-1033, 1963.
21. NILSSON, N.M.P: *Primitive Time-Reckoning.* Skrifter Utgivna av Humanistiska Vetenskapssamfundet i Lund, No. 1, 1920.
22. WERNER, H: *Comparative Psychology of Mental Development.* New York, Follett, 1948.
23. CUNNISON, I: History on the Luapula. *The Rhodes-Livingston Papers.* London, Oxford University Press, 1951.
24. PIERIS, R: Character Formation and the Acquisitive Society. *Psychiatry, 15*:53-60, 1952.
25. FOOTE, N.N: The autonomy of the consumer. In Clark, L.H. (ed.): *Consumer Behavior.* New York University Press, 1954, p. 17.

Chapter 6

SUBJECTIVE TIME IN MYTH AND LITERATURE

I

THE REPRESENTATION OF TIME in the myths of archaic peoples is far removed from the simple beat of an internal clock. By myth I do not mean fable but, following Eliade,[1,2] that which archaic societies believe to be absolute truth because it is a record of a primordial, sacred history. Time in myth has neither a fixed metric nor a uniform flow. It is apprehended rather as possessing properties derived from events.[3] A day remains memorable in the calendar of archaic peoples if once in the remote past it was the occasion of a sacred happening. Equally, a day can commemorate a calamity, and remain, in perpetuity, a day of mourning. In archaic societies, time, like space, eventually becomes structured. Every period of time, like every zone of space, is either sacred or profane, lucky or unlucky. Hesiod's *Works and Days* provides a calendar of the months and days which are propitious or unpropitious for different tasks or occupations; each period is animated by a personal spirit. The ancient pseudo-science of astrology is geared to this structurization of time. In the *Iliad* of Homer, time has one quality for the victor and another for the vanquished, and so it acquires the character of fate or destiny.[4] Hence, Euripides represents justice as depending on impersonal time. In general, archaic thinking sees the success or failure of an enterprise as a function of where and when it takes place.

There is another feature of time in myth which distinguishes it from the modern man's notion of time. In myth, past and future may merge into the present, so that sometimes all three become one, the present moment being laden with the past and pregnant with the future. In attenuated form, we perpetuate this fusion of past and present of time when, on a solemn anniversary, we recollect an event that happened long ago. The 2-minute silence on 11th November (Armistice Day) is blended in our minds with the moment in 1918 when World War I was brought to an end. But we do not, as in myth, credit a day retrospectively with an event that has not yet taken place. An example of this occurs in Biblical myth. We are told that when the three Angels visited the matriarch

FIGURE 8. Daumier's *The Past, the Present and the Future*. Reproduced by Courtesy of The Metropolitan Museum of Art, Dick Fund, 1941.

Sarah, to announce that, at the age of 90, she would bear a child, she served them with unleavened bread, because it would be on the anniversary of that day some 400 years *later* at the time of the Exodus from Egypt, that the *historic* unleavened bread would be made.

II

A form of this mythical time appears in our own day in ecstasy, dream and trance-like states. It also constitutes the framework for a number of films made by contemporary producers eager to free themselves from the constraints of clock and calendar; and the camera aids them in this extraordinary endeavour. Treated like space, time loses its irreversible character. The producer portrays the past, the present and the future of his characters in any order he likes, and he varies this order as he pleases. More than this, he compresses within hours or minutes events which, in actuality, have endured for years. Time's arrow is abolished while its normal scale is transformed.

The interpretation of time by archaic peoples and its representation in their myths is a relatively short step from the treatment of time in works of fiction. J. B. Priestley[5] has distinguished three modes of time in novels. The first is said to be characteristic of the man or woman born to write novels. These writers, says Priestley, maintain an even flow of narration, without any sudden spurts or interruptions. They travel in top gear, and though the narrative is greatly speeded up, by comparison with the actual time taken by the events described, it moves evenly, days, months and years being in their correct proportion.

The second mode is exemplified in writers like Dickens and Dostoevski, who accelerate, as it were, suddenly from first to top gear and *vice versa,* thus compelling the reader to alternate unexpectedly and dramatically from calm to high tension.

The third mode is in slow motion or even stationary, as illustrated, *par excellence,* in the work of Proust, and in that of Laurence Sterne, whom Proust greatly admired. A description of a brief episode, like Tristram Shandy's first two minutes, takes longer to read than the episode lasted in actuality. As is well known, Stendhal, James Joyce, Thomas Mann, Virginia Woolf and others of the same school deliberately exploited this technique. Ortega y Gasset[6] has remarked particularly on the "sluggishness" of the Proustian narrative: the prolongation of the moment is carried to its limit. "So slowly does the action move that it seems more like a sequence of ecstatic stillnesses without progress or tension." There is no plot worthy of the name and no dramatic interest, only pure "motionless description:" the river of time is frozen. Perhaps it is in such a sense that the timelessness of the Freudian unconscious is to be understood. What takes place is a detemporalization of experience, if such a clumsy word is allowed.

III

Since one man's myth is another man's religion, we need not here distinguish the two. All the great religions have developed their own characteristic conception of time. Unlike the myths of "primitive" peoples, which tend to be preoccupied with the beginnings of things, the more advanced cults are turned towards the shape of things to come in the end. In Chinese Taoism, the flux of time is illusory and must be overcome by ensuring an indefinitely long future which faithfully perpetuates the past. The ancient Egyptians found a similar solution for the conquest of Time by looking to a future in which the present is securely embalmed, in all its minutest details. Buddhism, too, seeks a future protected against all accidental change, but this is to be achieved by an obliteration of the past, in Nirvana, rather than by its perpetuation. In the Indian Upanishads, Nirvana is represented as the way of escape from Time, from which springs all pain and suffering. Persian myth conceives Time as the stage for a contest of cosmic dimensions between Ormuzd and Ahriman, the forces of light and darkness; while Biblical and Christian thought see Time as theophany, a medium for the manifestation of divine purpose.[7]

This brief sketch of diverse visions of time has omitted a particular feature which is shared by the Indo-Graeco-Roman & other archaic cultures and is by no means, even today, a thing of the past. I refer to the cyclical notion of time, a drama repeatedly re-enacted, history ever repeating itself *ad infinitum,* by contrast with an onward progression of events each of which is unique and never occurs again. On the cyclical view, history is but a calendar on a vaster plane.[8] Thus, Chinese thought contains cyclical and linear elements but has one cyclical system which recommences every sixty years, and the cycles in Indian myth consist of four epochs of unequal duration, beginning with the longest and ending with the shortest.

The designations of these Indian epochs, as Eliade[9] has remarked, are taken from the names of throws in the play of dice. The notion of cyclical time is a way of expressing the motif of gambling. The longer the sequence of a true gambler's failures, the stronger his conviction that he will succeed in the end. Hence, as his losses mount, he is ready to hazard a greater stake. Now in the Indian, as in other cyclical systems, the contemporary epoch is looked upon as decadent by comparison with what went before; and even in the contemporary period, the moment progressively worsens. All this speaks of a gambler's optimism, for the worsening situation is felt to carry a seed of regeneration. The essence of the cyclical conception of time is that a stage is reached at which the world comes to an end and then recommences afresh. Perhaps this is a measure of defence against decay which comes with the passage of time.

Cyclical notions survive in modern societies which supposedly have adopted a rectilinear conception of historical time. When we extend a wish for a "Happy New Year," we never attempt to stretch the wish for *two* years. We feel somehow that this would not be valid, that the term of the wish expires at the end of the year, just as the validity of a railway ticket expires after a specified period.

IV

We owe to antiquity two basic images of time. First, the Greek *kairos,* a decisive choice-point in the human situation, represented by the figure of Opportunity, a man with wings on shoulders and heels, a forelock by which he can be seized, scales precariously balanced on a knife's edge and the wheel of Fortune. Such representations were familiar until the eleventh century, when, in the image of Fortune, they blended the idea of unstable equilibrium with that of transience. By a slight change, the image may be made to represent Time in general, as in The Apotheosis of Homer, in which winged time bears the *Iliad* and the *Odyssey*. *Kairos,* the moment of opportunity, is a special moment, the *conjuncture* of the astrologers, when the time is ripe and opportune. More than any-

FIGURE 9. Aion, with signs of the zodiac. Second-third century. Museo-Profano, Vatican.

thing else, it is the choice of an auspicious instant that counts for success.[10]

A second image, from Iranian sources, is *Aion,* a symbol of divine and inexhaustible creativeness, associated with the cult of Mithra. *Aion* too is a winged figure but with the head and claws of a lion wound round by a snake and holding a key in each hand. A variation of this theme is found in the representation of *Phanes,* the winged Orphic god, who appears as a youth, surrounded by signs of the zodiac, representing power and fertility.

The antique images stood for abundance, vigour and youth. Emblems of decrepitude and decay, such as the hour-glass, crutches and the scythe or sickle, are a later development, possibly by error, due to the confusion of Chronos, "father of all things," with *Kronos,* patron of agriculture and oldest and most formidable of the gods. Plutarch[11] has been held responsible for transmitting if not originating this confusion. "Why," he asks, "do they repute *Saturn (Kronos)* the father of Truth? Is it for that (as some philosophers deem) they are of the opinion that *Saturn (Kronos)* is Time? and Time you know well findeth out and revealeth the Truth. Or because, as the poets fable, men lived under Saturn's reign in the Golden Age: and if the life of man was then most just and righteous, it followeth consequently that there was much truth in the world."

This confusion was perpetuated by the neo-Platonists, who saw in *Kronos* a symbol of cosmic mind *(noos).* His sickle, which could signify either agriculture or the castration of *Uranus,* may have been reinterpreted as a symbol of temporal corrosion; and the story that *Kronos* devoured his children came to be seen as Time consuming all things. This syncretism is evidently the source of the idea of Time as hostile and capricious, and of the portrayal of justice as a function of time, in the sense of fate, though this latter interpretation has an older birth. In Sophocles' *Antigone* we read: "Chance raises a man to the heights, chance casts him down," and Euripides, in *Antiope,* describes justice as "Time's Daughter;" in the fragment *Bellerophontes,* he writes:

"For Time, who from no Father springs, applies
His levell'd line, and shews man's foul misdeeds"

In the old Iranian epics, the words and expressions for Time often have the sense of fate or chance. Time is basically hostile to man, for Time carries the secrets of an unalterable destiny.[12]

Other qualities of subjective time found their way into mediaeval and Renaissance art. Reverdy, in the sixteenth century, treats Time and Chance as antagonists,[13] while in the allegorical paintings of Bronzino, Time, with wings and hour-glass is depicted as the Revealer, "unmasking falsehood and bringing truth to light."

FIGURE 10. *Man Prevented by Time from Seizing Chance,* by Georges Reverdy. Reproduced by courtesy of the Warburg Institute and Professor R. Wittkower.

Time's role as revealer has appeared in innumerable folk sayings and poems in which truth, virtue and innocence are revealed, rescued or vindicated by Time. These express the classical dictum: *veritas filia temporis* (Truth is the daughter of Time), of which two rather differing versions were current in ancient Greece: either Time reveals guilt or it reveals merit.[14] Subsequently, the idea of

FIGURE 11. Bronzino's *Venus, Cupid, Folly & Time*. Reproduced by courtesy of the Trustees, The National Gallery, London.

Time as guide to the light of Truth became the common property, in turn, of Greek comedy, Roman philosophy, the Fathers of the Church and Byzantine culture.

Apart from the two fundamental images that have come down from antiquity, a host of symbols of time have sprung from the imagination of poets. Shakespeare alone "has implored, challenged, berated and conquered Time in more than a dozen sonnets . . . He condenses and surpasses the speculations and emotions of many centuries:" "Wasteful time;" "Devouring time;" "Time's fickle glass;" "Time . . . delves the parallels in beauty's brow."[15]

V

The experimenter strives to identify the properties of the internal clock and to discern a system in its apparent caprice. He traces the isomorphism, such as it is, between private and public time-keeping. But the idea of time, in its plenitude, goes beyond this. It brings to mind an intimation of corrosion, decrepitude and decay, of inexorable aging, of dust returning to dust. Hence, man's ceaseless but unavailing efforts to arrest time, to discover the elixir of life and the secret of rejuvenation, to build monuments, pyramids and empires which can resist the teeth of time. Hence, too, the pursuit of a mirage of love which neither withers nor fades with time, and the dream of glory which is outside time. Whether we think of the food and weapons with which neolithic man equipped his dead for the continuation of life, or of the attempt made from time to time by the elderly to recapture youth by transfusing into themselves the blood of younger persons, the story is the same. And we witness, in our own day, the gallant efforts of cosmeticians and morticians to continue the never-ending battle with old age, death and time. The more man reflects on time, the more he realizes that "all our yesterdays have lighted fools the way to dusty death." "O time," confided Leonardo to his *Notebooks,* "consumer of all things! O envious age, thou destroyest all things; and devourest all things with the hard teeth of the years little by little, in slow death. When Helen of Troy looked in her mirror and saw the withered wrinkles which old age had made in her face, she wept and wondered why she had been twice seized and carried away."

A theory of time adequate to a world picture must encompass human experience as an integral part of nature. And this experience includes a confrontation with the certainty of death. In one sense, death is a biological event which comes at the end of one's days, but the knowledge that death must come is a life-long companion. The foreknowledge of death must find its place in a psychology of time which, as Proust affirmed, is as surely needed as a geometry of space, a psychology which should begin with the magic words: "Once upon a time," and should end: "And they lived happily ever after."

REFERENCES

1. ELIADE, M: *Images and Symbols* (transl., P. Mairet). London, Harvill Press, 1952.
2. ELIADE, M: *The Myth of the Eternal Return* (transl., W.R. Trask). New York, Pantheon Books, 1954.
3. CASSIRER, E: *The Philosophy of Symbolic Forms* (transl., R. Manheim). London, Oxford University Press, 1955, Vol. 2, pp. 104-105.
4. ONIANS, R.P: *The Origins of European Thought.* London, Cambridge University Press, 1951, pp. 411-415.
5. PRIESTLEY, J.B: *Man and Time.* London, Aldus Books, 1964, pp. 110-115.
6. GASSET, J. ORTEGA Y: *The Dehumanization of Art.* New York, Doubleday, 1956, pp. 74-75; see also Bonnot, R: Le roman du temps. *J. Psychol.,* July-Sept., 1956, pp. 454-72.
7. BRANDON, S.G.F: *History, Time and Deity.* Manchester, Manchester University Press, 1965, p. 5 *et seq.*
8. CAILLOIS, ROGER: Circular Time, Rectilinear Time. *Diogenes, 42*: 1-13, Summer, 1963.
9. ELIADE (1952): *op. cit.,* p.63.
10. PANOFSKY, E: *Studies in Iconology.* New York, Oxford University Press, 1939.
11. PLUTARCH: *The Romane Questions, Bibliothèque de Carabas,* Vol. VII, London, David Nutt, 1892, Item 12, p. 21.
12. RINGGREN, H: Dieu, le temps et le destin dans les épopées persanes. *J. Psychol., 3*:407-423, 1956.
13. WITTKOWER, R: Chance, time and virtue. *J. Warburg Inst., 1*:313-321, 1937-8.
14. SAXL, FRITZ: Veritas filia temporis. In Klibansky, R, and Paton, H.J. eds: *Philosophy and History.* Oxford, Clarendon Press, 1936, pp. 197-222.
15. PANOFSKY (1939): *op. cit.*

Chapter 7

TOWARDS A MODEL OF
PSYCHOLOGICAL TIME

I FIND IT HARD TO imagine how a model for psychological time could be set up from which one could predict all the diverse effects described in the preceding chapters. Yet a start has to be made, even on a limited basis, and we need not be inhibited by the fear that our model may only have a restricted explanatory value. The word "model," let us note, is variously employed in the literature of science. It may refer to a logical or mathematical representation of a set of ideas, at one extreme, or to a rough working sketch, at the other.[1] It may also be used in the sense of a metaphor or analogy or as a working miniature of what it represents. Such variety of usage suggests that there are different models of what a model should be. Ideally, I presume, a model should enable us to predict the outcome of experiments inspired by it. Here, however, we shall have to be less ambitious. We shall confine ourselves to a simple scheme which seems to integrate essential features of subjective time. More precise elaboration will have to be left to future investigation and analysis.

A suggestion we owe to M. Treisman[2] provides a good point of departure. He describes an ingenious model of psychological time which has three components, a pacemaker (proposed by Hoagland), a counter and a store. The pacemaker emits a continuous and regular series of pulses. The counter, in measuring an interval of experienced time, records the number of pulses passing a given point on the path leading from the pacemaker. Finally, this number is transferred from the counter to a store, which may retain the information in logarithmic form. If, for instance, the time interval between one pulse and the next is, say, 0.01 second, and the subject is presented with a clock interval of 2 seconds, the counter will count twenty pulses and transfer this number to the memory store as a record of the interval presented.

This model is useful in explaining several elements in the re-production of intervals of time. It also throws light on the nature of some kinds of error in temporal judgement. Nevertheless, it needs to be amplified if it is to embrace a more extended range of temporal experience.

Before we amplify the model, let us try to dispose of an old

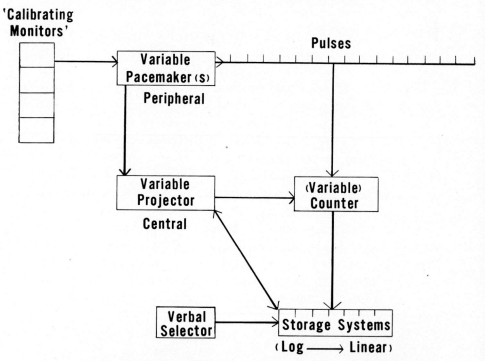

FIGURE 12. Modified Treisman model to include additional elements.

paradox. A period of clock time filled with absorbing activities or events seems to pass quickly, whilst idle time or time spent in tedious, dull or repetitive tasks seems to drag. Yet retrospectively, these effects are paradoxically reversed. The time spent in lively or gay fashion seems, on looking back, to be stretched out, whereas the empty or monotonously spent interval seems contracted. Both when the judgement of time is contemporaneous with the activity and when it is made retrospectively, the judgement has meaning only if we suppose that it is made against a background which is temporally uniform and with which the "rushing" and "dragging" are compared.

The paradox becomes less paradoxical if we bear in mind that when we are inactive against our will or engaged in a dull or tedious task, we are conscious of the passage of time as such. Subjective time in this respect is like the experience of pain. Just as there can be no pain, whatever the physical injury to limb or tissue, without attending to the subjective effects of the injury, so there can be no temporal experience without awareness of the emptiness of the long-drawn-out or unpleasant experience. By contrast, actively or joyfully filled time takes possession of our attention to such a degree that little if anything is left to devote to the awareness of the passage of time as such: "I was bored with doing nothing and the hours dragged like days;" "I was so absorbed that I failed to realize that my time was up." These two sentences, reflecting common experience, illustrate the contrast under discussion.

Treisman's model takes us a step further towards explanation. If the pacemaker runs more slowly when we are engaged in a dull task than when we are occupied in a more exciting task, fewer pulses are registered in a given unit of clock time. Hence, retrospectively, this period of clock time will seem to have passed more quickly in the former than in the latter situation.

There are two principal components which I should wish to add to the model. In the first place, it must be emphasized that the pacemaker is to be considered variable, the variability being due to the effect of other experiences undergone at the same time as the temporal experience with which we are primarily concerned. These other experiences may be designated "calibrating monitors."[3] In the second place, I would add a variable projector. The point of this second suggestion is that some phenomena of temporal experience may, I believe, be explained by assuming that we possess projecting equipment apart from the recording equipment embodied in the pacemaker and counter. Our judgements of time are thus supposed to take account of the rate at which experiences are projected into awareness when we reproduce them, as well as of the rate at which they are initially recorded. We may, perhaps, make this a little clearer if we conceive the pacemaker-counter to work as a camera, and the variable projector to operate rather like film projecting apparatus. Both the camera and its associated but independent projector may be made to work at variable speeds, and many sorts of paradoxical and distorting effects can be produced by projecting the frames at a faster or slower rate than the one at which they were recorded, not to speak of projecting them in reverse time order. Let me briefly attempt to justify the addition of the two components to the model.

We begin by suggesting that the use of the word clock to refer to our internal time-keeping system may be misleading. In this respect, it may resemble the use of the expression "electronic brain" to describe a computer. Physical clocks, when functioning normally, whether they are water or sand clocks, mechanical, electrical, quartz or atomic clocks, share the property of "beating" at a constant rate. The units of time are not subject to variation in size from one day to the next. A clock minute in the morning has the same duration as a minute in the afternoon, an hour in the summer is identical in duration with an hour in the winter. By contrast, everyday observation, clinical evidence and experiment all testify to the inequality of subjective moments.

In terms of the model, this means that the pacemaker generates a variable number of pulses from one clock-moment to the next. Some of the variability of the pacemaker is attributable, as we have seen in Chapter 1, to temperature, and there is evidence that effects of changes in temperature are similar to effects of metabolic changes due to age, and to the effects of stimulant or depressant drugs. There are also other sources of stimulation, internal and external, which serve to pace our subjective time-keeping. Thus, our various *kappa* effects (see Chapter 4) illustrate the dependence of apparent duration on coexperienced visual distance, auditory pitch and passive movement.

Other investigators[3,4] have shown that, under certain conditions, the estimation of intervals of time is clearly influenced by the level of auditory stimulation but hardly at all by the level of visual stimulation. In an experiment which demonstrates this, the subjects were presented with a tone or illumination the duration of which was set randomly at 1, 2, 4, 8 or 16 seconds. Their task was to respond, after the interval, by pressing a button that re-set the tone or illumination for what seemed to them to be the same duration. Background conditions of light or dark during the presentation of the signal could be changed to dark or light while the subject was making his response; and initial quiet or noise could likewise be changed to subsequent noise or quiet, that is, during the response. The results show that a change from darkness to illumination (or *vice versa)* had no effect on apparent duration, but this was not the case with a change from noise to quiet (or *vice versa*). Signals which were presented noiselessly yielded subjective durations under conditions of noise that were, in fact, much longer than durations yielded under noiseless conditions following signals presented in noise. The investigators concluded that auditory stimulation constitutes a "calibrating monitor" which paces the internal clock.

Experiments by Mr. Brent Skelly, a student at our laboratory, point to a comparable differential effect of visual and auditory signals respectively. His subjects had to equate the duration of a tone with a standard duration of a light signal or, the other way round, they had to equate the duration of a light with a standard duration of a tone. In general, regardless of the order of presentation, and at frequencies ranging from 400 to 1,500 cycles per second, the subject allotted a duration to the tone which was shorter than the actual duration of the light signal, and he allotted a duration to the light which was longer than the actual duration of the tone. Taking all frequencies into consideration, the mean ratio of the two durations was 0.9 when the standard signal was light and 1.3 when it was a tone. From this we may infer that if a light signal is followed by an auditory signal of equal duration (or *vice versa),* the subject will tend to judge the duration of the auditory signal as the longer of the two.

The upshot of these remarks is to suggest that apparent duration, conceived as depending on the number of subjective pulses per unit of clock time, is not a uniform experience. Its units contract and expand as a function of particular influences to which we are subject at the time. It is these which, I submit, could be named "calibrating monitors."

In turning now to the variable projector, I should like to refer again to Hughlings Jackson's observation on the rapidity of neural discharge in epileptic seizures. This high rate of discharge, which is presumably independent of the peripheral pacemaker, causes loss of consciousness because there is no longer any sense of the passage of time. At the other end of the continuum, when there is a more or less complete absence of neural discharge, as for example, in hypothermia or clinical death, there is also loss of consciousness, including awareness of the passage of time. Between these extremes there is a zone within which the rate of neural discharge allows of temporal experience.

We may suppose that the central projector fluctuates with the varying rates of neural discharge which result from cerebral abnormality, drugs (stimulant or tranquillizer), hypnosis, intense emotion or the recollection of an event in the past charged with deep feeling.

A peripheral pacemaker by itself would be unable to account for the fact that when we are not merely estimating durations but recollecting earlier experiences, or entertaining imaginary sequences, we may mentally re-live in a few seconds or minutes events that in actuality require days or months. It is chiefly to account for these phenomena that we postulate a variable projector, operating more or less independently of the pacemaker. An extreme example of the operation of the projector would be the alleged experience of a drowning man who, it is often said, sees his whole life, or much of it, flash before his mind's eye in a second or two. The projector may be presumed not only to project outwards, that is, to awareness or conscious experience, but also towards the memory store, thereby affecting subsequent recall of the experiences.

Furthermore, reference to a single pacemaker may be an oversimplification. If we assume the existence of multiple pacemakers working in relative independence of one another, we might clarify problems that have not fallen within the range of our discussion so far. Thus, for example, there is a form of stuttering which is conceivably due to an asynchronization between thought and speech. Unlike the stammerer whose speech, for reasons which do not concern us here, is emotionally blocked, there is another kind of stutterer who has no speech impediment or blockage. His utterance simply cannot keep pace with his thinking. His thoughts sweep swiftly on while his speech, struggling to keep up the pace, lags behind. Normal persons differ very considerably in their rate of speech which, we may suppose, is geared to their rate of thinking. In the stuttering under consideration, the discrepancy between the two rates is too great for speech to maintain its smooth and intelligible flow: the hypothetical pacemakers for speech and thought are running at different speeds.

So far as the memory store is concerned, we can accept the suggestion that this may have a logarithmic character in the light of the evidence set forth in Chapter 3. But this is more complicated than appears at first sight. Comparative estimates of the time that has elapsed since, say, two past events, three months and one month ago respectively, seem directly related to the logarithms of the two intervals. But as the two events recede into the past, beyond, say, a year from now, the estimates assume a linear relationship with the chronological intervals. Hence we have to imagine that the nature of the store is such that the events registered in it are continuously being recoded with respect to their seeming remoteness from us in time.

As I have suggested in Chapter 3, estimates of the intervals of time that have elapsed since neutral events may follow a different rule from those relating to events or experiences highly charged with emotion. If we can take the intuitions of Leonardo and Proust as a serious basis for scientific hypothesis, we may suppose that the apparent temporal proximity of past events depends on the degree of their emotional significance. Taking analogous human judgements as a guide, such as those that arise in auditory experience, we might say that our feeling of the temporal proximity of a past experience varies as the logarithm of a measure of its emotional intensity.

Our model should also allow for the fact that our temporal estimates of future events seem to vary exponentially with the interval, by which I mean, of course, an "interval" as momentarily conceived, not in physical actuality.

In its amplified form, the model, rough and ready though it is, may hold promise of explaining some, at least, of the phenomena discussed in the first five chapters. Aberrations of temporal judgement may possibly be accounted for in terms of highly individual "calibrating monitors" which have developed in the patient's earlier experiences, or in terms of anomalies in the memory store. On the other hand, the model is of little help in explaining the child's judgements of duration, which may depend on the maturation of a coordinating process. We know that young children find great difficulty in estimating the duration of an object that has moved from A to B, if, at the same time, he is also observing a second object moving at a different speed. The intrusion of differential distances and velocities hampers the child's judgement of duration as such.

There are, too, the aspects of subjective time that come to the fore in myth, literature and art. These are of an order quite different from those we have been dealing with so far. So they cannot be incorporated in the kind of model we have been discussing. Time in myth, literature and art is the result of *reflection on* experience, a construction superimposed on apparent duration. Such constructions, based as they are on complex systems of beliefs, display varying degrees of elaboration, as exemplified in the religious cults of antiquity, each with its distinctive consciousness and valuation of time. In general, the conception of time in Indo-Graeco-Roman cultures was cyclical or bounded. As late as 1658, James Ussher, Archbishop of Armagh, fixed the date of creation at 22 October, 4004 B.C. The recognition of unbounded time forced itself on thinkers as recently as the eighteenth century.[5] This was more than a Copernican revolution, for it transformed the entire subsequent development of theory in most branches of science. The final breaching of the time-barrier in science was left to Charles Lyell, a pioneer of nineteenth century geology, and his efforts left their mark on the sister science of zoology. Of all the features that distinguish the science of today from the science of the Greeks, none is so distinctive as the acknowledgment of the role of Time.

In conclusion, let me rapidly retrace the path we have followed in this book. The discovery that psychological time is distinct from physical time is barely a century old, and is due to the great physicist-psychologist, Ernst Mach. No one before him had expressly distinguished time as privately, subjectively or intuitively experienced from time as measured by a clock or by the procession of days, months and years. Even the subtle self-analysis of St. Augustine in the fourth century failed to make the distinction.

Since the pioneer work of Mach, considerable progress has been made in the study of subjective time: in its micro-structure, in the measurement of comparatively long intervals (months, years) of past time, in the mapping of the subjective future and in the manner in which temporal information is stored in our memories.

Mach and the investigators who followed him were preoccupied with the attempt to measure estimates of different intervals of clock time under varying experimental conditions. A recent development has been to examine the subjective interdependence of time, distance and speed. Analysis of the interrelations between these basic dimensions of experience reveals a systematic pattern. How long we think we have travelled depends on how far and how fast we have travelled, just as how far we think we have travelled depends on the duration and speed of the journey, and how fast on its duration and distance. This pattern is already manifest in early childhood, but it is a changing pattern, which is only stabilized when intelligence reaches a mature level. Allied experiments reveal a related interdependence of visual and auditory time.

Like all our adult ideas, the concept of time has an individual history leading back to the early years of childhood. We can trace, through the developmental years, the manner in which a child perceives, judges and conceives time. From this we learn that the child begins as a relativist, not as an absolutist, a sequence which finds its parallel in the development of geometrical ideas and in the growth of speech.

Apart from the micro- and macro-structure of psychological time, its relativity and psychogenesis, there is another domain of great interest. This is the psychopathology of time, comprising the temporal aberrations characteristic of patients suffering from brain damage or mental disorder, as well as by the normal person in states of emotional excitement, in dreams, in hypnosis or under the influence of drugs. And finally, there are the rich manifestations of psychological time in myth and literature and in the history of art and religion.

A systematization of the forms of experience of time is necessary for an understanding of memory and thought processes as well as for the theory of perception. And in the affective life of man, the profoundest experiences of regret and nostalgia, on the one hand, and of anticipation and hope, on the other, are only intelligible in relation to feelings of time. All this calls for integration in terms of a model which represents the extreme of subjectivity coupled with the extreme of objectivity. The first step towards such a synthesis was implicit in Arrhenius' equation, which has been introduced into biology, physiology and psychology in terms of the notion of an internal clock or pacemaker. Further clarification of the complexities of psychological time seems to come from the assumption that we record and reproduce the passage of time in a manner analogous to the way a camera and a projector can be coupled in taking and projecting a film. This is a first approximation to what is bound eventually to become a much more intricate representation, if it is to do justice to the paradoxes and mysteries of inner time.

REFERENCES

1. APOSTEL, L: Towards the formal study of models in non-formal sciences. *Synthese, 12*:125-161, 1960.
2. TREISMAN, M: Psychology of Time. *Discovery,* October, 1965, pp. 41-45.
3. HIRSCH, I.J., BILGER, R.C., and DEATHERAGE, B.H: The effect of auditory and visual background on apparent duration. *Amer.J. Psychol., 69*:561-574, 1956.
4. CREELMAN, DOUGLAS, C: Human discrimination of auditory duration. *J.Acoust.Soc.Amer., 34*:582-593, 1962.
5. TOULMIN, S., and GOODFIELD, J: *The Discovery of Time*. London, Hutchinson, 1965.

BIBLIOGRAPHY

ABBE, M: The spatial effect upon the perception of time. *Jap.J.Exp. Psychol., 3*:1-52, 1936.

ABBE, M: The spatial effect upon the perception of time: Simultaneous comparison of phenomenal size of two time intervals divided by three stimuli. *Jap.J.Exp. Psychol., 4*:1-12, 1937.

ABBE, M: The temporal effect upon the perception of space. *Jap.J. Exp.Psychol., 4*:83-93, 1937.

ABE, S: Experimental study on the correlation between time and space. *Tohoku Psychologia Folia, 3*:53-68, 1935.

APOSTEL, LEO: Towards the formal study of models in the non-formal sciences. *Synthese, 12*:125-161, 1960.

BELL, C.R., and PROVINS, K.A: Relation between physiological responses to environmental heat and time judgements. *J.Exp.Psychol., 66*:572-579, 1963.

BELL, C.R: Time estimation and increases in body temperature. *J.Exp. Psychol., 70*:232-234, 1965.

BENUSSI, V: *Psychologie der Zeitauffassung*. Heidelberg, Carl Winter's Universitätsbuchhandlung, 1913.

BONAPARTE, MARIE: Time and the unconscious. *Int.J.Psychoanal., 21*: 427-68, 1940; see also Meyerhoff, H: *Time in Literature*. Berkeley and Los Angeles, University of California Press, 1955, pp. 153-154.

BORING, E.G: *A History of Experimental Psychology*. New York, Appleton-Century-Crofts, 1929.

BORING, E.G: *Sensation and Perception in the History of Experimental Psychology*. New York, Appleton-Century-Crofts, 1942.

BORING, LUCY D., and BORING, E.G: Temporal judgements after sleep. *Studies in Psychology* (Titchener Commemorative Volume). Worcester, Mass, Wilson, 1917, pp. 255-279.

BRAMWELL, J. MILNE: *Hypnotism*. London, Thomas Yoseloff, 1960 (first published, 1903).

BRANDON, S.G.F: *History, Time and Deity*. Manchester, Manchester University Press, 1965, p. 5 *et seq.*

BRECHER, G.A: Die Entstehung und Biologische, Bedeutung der Subjektiven Zeiteinheit—des Momentes. *Z. vergleichende Physiol.* (Berlin), *18*:204-243, 1932-33.

BROAD, C.D: *Scientific Thought.* London, Routledge & Kegan Paul, 1923.

BROMBERG, A: Marihuana intoxication. *Amer. J. Psychiat., 91*:303-330, 1934.

BÜNNING, E: *The Physiological Clock.* Berlin, Springer Verlag, 1964.

BUTLER, SAMUEL: *The World of the Unborn, Erewhon.* London, Jonathan Cape, 1872, p. 191.

CAILLOIS, ROGER: Circular Time, Rectilinear Time. *Diogenes, 42*:1-13, Summer, 1963.

CASSIRER, E: *The Philosophy of Symbolic Forms* (transl., R. Manheim). London, Oxford University Press, 1955, Vol. 2, pp. 104-5.

CLAPARÈDE, E: La genèse de l'hypothèse. *Arch Psychol., 24*:1-55, 1933.

CLAUSEN, J: An evaluation of experimental methods of time judgement. *J. Exp. Psychol., 40*:756-761, 1950.

COHEN, JOHN, HANSEL, C.E.M., and WALKER, D.B: The time taken to decide as a measure of subjective probability. *Acta Psychol. (Amst.), 17*:177-183, 1960.

COHEN, JOHN, HANSEL, C.E.M., and SYLVESTER, J.D: An experimental study of comparative judgements of time. *Brit. J. Psychol., 55*:108-114, 1954.

COHEN, JOHN: The concept of goal gradients. *J. Gen. Psychol., 49*:303-308, 1953.

COHEN, JOHN: *Chance, Skill and Luck.* Harmondsworth, Pelican Books, 1960, see Chapter 9.

COHEN, JOHN, DEARNALEY, E.J., and HANSEL, C.E.M: A quantitative study of meaning. *Brit. J. Educ. Psychol., 28*: Pt. II, 141-148, 1958.

COHEN, JOHN, HANSEL, C.E.M., and SYLVESTER, J.D: Interdependence of temporal and auditory judgements. *Nature, 174*:642, 1954.

COHEN, JOHN, COOPER, P., and ONO, AKIO: The hare and the tortoise: A study of the *tau*-effect in walking and running. *Acta Psychol. (Amst.), 21*:387-393, 1963.

COHEN, JOHN, HANSEL, C.E.M., and SYLVESTER, J.D: A new phenomenon in the judgement of time. *Nature, 172*:901, 1953.

COHEN, JOHN, HANSEL, C.E.M., and SYLVESTER, J.D: Interdependence in judgements of space, time and movement. *Acta Psychol. (Amst.), 11*:360-372, 1955.

COHEN, JOHN, and COOPER, P: New phenomena in apparent duration, distance and speed. *Nature, 196*:1233-1234, 1962.

COHEN, JOHN, and COOPER, P: Durée, longueur et vitesse apparentes d'un voyage. *L' Année Psychol.,* No. *1*:13-28, 1963.

COHEN, JOHN: Psychological time. *Sci. Amer.*, November, 1964, pp. 116-124.

COHEN, JOHN: The scientific revolution and leisure. *Nature, 198*:1028-1033, 1963.

COHEN, JOHN, HANSEL, C.E.M., and SYLVESTER, J.D: Mind wandering. *Brit. J. Psychol., 47*:61-62, 1956.

COHEN, JOHN. *Behaviour in Uncertainty*. London, Allen & Unwin, 1964 (New York, Basic Books, 1965).

COLERIDGE, S.T: *Biographia Literaria*. London, Dent, 1908, p. 62.

COOPER, L.F, *et al.*: *Time Distortion in Hypnosis*. Baltimore, Williams & Wilkins, 1959 (2nd ed).

CREELMAN, C.DOUGLAS: Human discrimination of auditory duration. *J.Acoust. Soc. Amer., 34*:582-593, 1962.

CUNNISON, I: History on the Luapula. *The Rhodes-Livingston Papers.* London, Oxford University Press, 1951.

DE LA MARE, WALTER: *Desert Islands*. London, Faber & Faber, 1932, pp.91-96.

Diurnal rhythms in human physiological processes. In *Command 2787,* Report of the Medical Research Council, October 1963, March 1965. London, Her Majesty's Stationery Office, 1965.

EKMAN, G., and FRANKENHAEUSER, M: Subjective time scales, *Rep. Psychol. Lab Univ. Stockholm* No. *49.*, 1957.

ELIADE, M: *Myths, Dreams and Mysteries* (trans., P. Mairet). London, Harvill Press, 1960.

ELIADE, M: *Images and Symbols* (trans., P. Mairet). London, Harvill Press, 1952.

ELIADE, M: *The Myth of the Eternal Return* (transl., W. R. Trask). New York, Pantheon Books, 1954.

FRAISSE, P: *The Psychology of Time* (transl., Jennifer Leith). New York, Harper & Row, 1963, pp.262-280.

FRANCOIS, M: Contribution a l'étude du sens du temps. La température interne comme facteur de variation de l'appréciation subjectives des durées. *L' Année Psychol., 28*:188-204, 1927; Influence de la temperature interne sur notre appreciation du temps. *C. R. Soc. Biol., 108:*201-203, 1928.

FRANKENHAEUSER, M: *Estimation of Time*. Stockholm, Almquist & Wiksell, 1959.

FENICHEL, O: *The Psycho-Analytical Theory of the Neuroses*. New York, Holt 1943, p.296.

FOOTE, N.N.: The autonomy of the consumer. In Clark, L. H. (ed.): *Consumer Behaviour,* New York University Press, 1954, p.17.

FREUD, S: *New Introductory Lectures on Psycho-Analysis.* New York, Norton, 1933, p.105.

FREUD, S: *Beyond the Pleasure Principle* (transl., C.J.M. Hubback) London, Hogarth Press, 1942, p.32.

GASSET, J. ORTEGA y: *The Dehumanization of Art.* New York, Doubleday, 1956, pp.74-5; see also Bonnot, R: Le roman du temps, *J. Psychol.,* July-Sept., 1956, pp.454-72.

GELDREICH, E.W: A lecture room demonstration of the visual *tau* effect. *Amer. J. Psychol., 46:*483, 1934.

GILLILAND, A.R., HOFELD, J.B., and ECKSTRAND, G: Studies in time perception. *Psychol. Bull., 43:*162-176, 1946.

GREGG, L.W: Fractionation of temporal intervals. *J. Exp. Psychol., 42:*307-312, 1951.

GUILFORD, J.P: Spatial symbols in the apprehension of time. *Amer. J. Psychol., 37:*420-423, 1926.

GUNN, J. ALEXANDER: *The Problem of Time.* London, Allen & Unwin, 1929.

HARKER, JANET E: Biological clocks. *Discovery,* April, 1961, pp.138-142.

HEDIGER, H: *Studies of the Psychology and Behavior of Animals in Zoos and Circuses* (trans., G. Sircom). London, Butterworth, 1955, p.64 also citing Buck, J.B: *Quart. Rev. Biol., 13:*1938.

HELSON, H: The *tau*-effect—An example of psychological relativity. *Science, 71:*536-537, 1930.

HELSON, H., and KING, S.M: The *tau*-effect—An example of pychological relativity. *J.Exp.Psychol., 14:*202-217, 1931.

HIRSH, I.J: Auditory perception of temporal order. *J.Acoust.Soc.Amer., 31:*759-767, 1959.

HIRSH, I.J., BILGER, R.C., and DEATHERAGE, B.H: The effect of auditory and visual background on apparent duration. *Amer.J.Psychol., 69:*561-574, 1956.

HOAGLAND, H: The physiological control of judgements of duration: Evidence for a chemical clock. *J.Gen.Psychol., 9:*267-287, 1933; Consciousness and the chemistry of time. *Problems of Consciousness.* In Abramson, H.A. (ed.): Josiah Macy, 1951, pp. 164-178.

JACKSON, HUGHLINGS: *Selected Writings.* (Taylor, J. [ed.]). London, Staples Press, Vol. I, 1960.

JAHODA, G: Children's Concepts of Time and History. *Edu. Rev., 15:* 87-104, 1963.

JONES, E: *Essays in Applied Psycho-Analysis.* London, Hogarth Press, 1951, pp. 257-9.

KALMUS, H: Communication with animals. *New Scientist,* 11 February, 1963, pp. 372-5.

LEONARD, K: Eigenartige Tagesschwankungen des Zustandbildes bei Parkinsonismus, *Z. Ges. Neurol. Psychiat., 134*:76, 1931.

LIDDELL, H.S: *Emotional Hazards in Animals and Man.* Springfield, Illinois: C. C Thomas, 1959; and also *Discussions on Child Development* (Tanner, J.M., and Inhelder, B. [eds.], Vol. 2. London, Tavistock Publications, 1956, p. 144.

LUCRETIUS: *De Natura Rerum* (transl., H.A.J.Munro). London, Bell, 1914.

MACH, E: *Contributions to the Analysis of Sensations* (transl., C.M. Williams). Chicago, Open Court Publ. Co., 1897 (1st German edition, 1886).

MacLEOD, R.B., and ROFF, M.F: An experiment in temporal disorientation. *Acta Psychol. (Amst.), 1*:381-423, 1936.

MALRIEU, PH: Le probléme de la conscience du passé. *J. Psychol.,* Jan.-June, 1954, pp. 91-108; Le social et le temps de l'enfant. *J.de Psychol.,* July-Sept. 1956, pp. 315-32.

MEYERHOFF, H: *Time in Literature.* Berkeley & Los Angeles, University of California Press, 1955.

MILLS, J.N.: Human circadian rhythms. *Physiol. Rev.,* 1966, *46*:128-171.

NEITZSCHE, F: *The Genealogy of Morals.* London, Foulis, 1910.

NILSSON, N.M.P: *Primitive Time-Reckoning.* Skrifter Utgivna av Humanistiska Vetenskapssamfundet i Lund, No. 1, 1920.

ONIANS, R.P: *The Origins of European Thought.* London, Cambridge University Press, 1951, pp.411-415.

PANOFSKY, E: *Studies in Iconology.* New York, Oxford University Press, 1939.

PIAGET, J: *Le développement de la notion de temps chez l'enfant.* Paris, Presses Universitaires de France, 1946.

PIAGET, J: The development of time concepts in the child. In Hoch, Paul H., and Zubin, J. (eds.): *Psychopathology of Childhood.* London, Grune & Stratton, 1955, pp. 34-44.

PIAGET, J: Psychology and philosophy. In Wolman, B. J., and Nagel, E. (eds.): *Scientific Psychology.* New York, Basic Books, 1965, pp. 28-43.

PIERIS, R: Character formation and the acquisitive society. *Psychiatry, 15*:53-60, 1952.

PIÉRON, H: *The Sensations* (transl., M.H.Pirenne and B.C.Abbott). London, Muller, 1952.

PIÉRON, H: Les problèmes psychophysiologiques de la perception du temps. *L' Année Psychol., 24*:1-25, 1923.

PITTENDRIGH, C.S., and BRUCE, V.G: An oscillator model for biological clocks. *Rhythmic and Synthetic Processes in Growth.* Princeton, Princeton University Press, 1957, pp. 75-109.

PLUTARCH: *The Romane Questions, Bibliothèque de Carabas,* Vol. VII. London, David Nutt, 1892, Item 12, p. 21.

PORTMANN, A: Preface to a science of man. *Diogenes, 3*:40, 1962.

PORTMAN, A: Time in the life of the organism. *Man and Time, Papers from the Eranos Yearbooks.* London, Routledge, 1958, pp. 310-311; see also Brecher, G.A: Die Entstehung und biologische Bedeutung der subjektiven Zeiteinheit,—des Momentes. *Z. vergleichende Physiol. (Berlin), XVIII*:204-243, 1932-33.

PRIESTLEY, J.B: *Man and Time.* London, Aldus Books, 1964, pp. 110-115.

PROUST, M: *Lettres à René Blum, Bernard Grasset, Louis Brun,* p. 61. In Poulet, Georges: *Studies in Human Time* (transl., Elliott Coleman). Baltimore, Johns Hopkins Press, 1956, pp. 304-5.

RICHTER, C.P: Biological clocks in medicine and psychiatry: Shock phase hypothesis, *Proc.Nat.Acad.Sci. U.S.A., 46*:1506-1530, 1960.

RINGGREN, H: Dieu, le temps et le destin dans les épopées persanes, *J. Psychol., 3*:407-423, 1956.

ROSS, S., and KATCHMAR, L: The construction of a magnitude function for short-time intervals. *Amer.J.Psychol., 64*:397-401, 1951.

SAXL, FRITZ: Veritas filia temporis. In Klibansky, R., and Paton, H.J: *Philosophy and History.* Oxford. Clarendon Press, 1936, pp. 197-222.

SCHAEFER, V.G., and GILLILAND, A.R: The relation of time estimation to certain physiological changes. *J.Exp.Psychol., 23*:545-552, 1938.

SCHILDER, P: The psychopathology of time. *J.Nerv.Ment.Dis., 33*:530-546, 1936.

SCHMIDT, H.D., and ZARN, R: Erfolg und Misserfolg als Determinanten einiger Entscheidungsparameter. *Z. Psychol., 69*:18-34, 1964.

SIFFRE, MICHEL: *Beyond Time.* London, Chatto & Windus, 1965.

STEVENS, S.S: On the psychophysical law. *Psychol.Rev., 64*:153-181, 1957.

STROUD, J.M.: The fine structure of psychological time. pp. 174-205, In *Information Theory in Psychology.* Quastler, H. (ed.): Glencoe, Ill., The Free Press, 1955.

TOULMIN, S., and GOODFIELD, J: *The Discovery of Time.* London, Hutchinson, 1965.

TREISMAN, M: Temporal discrimination and the indifference interval: Implications for a model of the "internal clock." *Physiol. Monog.,* 77:Whole No. 576, 1963.

TREISMAN, M: The psychology of time. *Discovery,* October, 1965, pp. 41-45.

VON CHAMISSO, A: *The Marvellous History of the Shadowless Man.* London, Holden & Hardingham, 1913, p. 43.

WALLACE, M., and RABIN, A.I: Temporal experience. *Psychol.Bull., 57:* 213-236, 1960.

WERNER, H: *Comparative Psychology of Mental Development.* New York, Follett, 1948.

WITTKOWER, R: Chance, time and virtue. *J.Warburg Inst., 1:*313-321, 1937-38.

WOODROW, H: Time perception. pp. 1224-1236. In Stevens, S.S. (ed.): *Handbook of Experimental Psychology.* New York, Wiley, 1951.

INDEX

A

Alarm clock effect
  examples of, 35
  explanations for, 10
Amnesia, 60
Anabiosis, 4
Apparent Duration
  and age, 54
  interrelation with speed and distance, 54, 55
  scales of, 21-22
  sensory differences, 14, 15, 16
  Arhenius' equation, 4

B

Bakhmetyev, P., 4
Bell, C.R., 4, 5
Benussi, V., 40
Boring, E.G., 10
Broad, C.D., 35

C

Calibrating monitors, 85, 87, 90
Calibration of the day, 67-68
Circadian rhythms, 6, 7, 30
  effects of disease, 7, 8
  effects of experiment, 30
  effects of operations, 7
  physiological basis of, 8
Clocks, physical, 86
Coleridge, Samuel Taylor, 18
Counter, 83-4, 86
Culture and time, 68, 69
Cyclical nature of time, 75

D

Da Vinci, Leonardo, 33, 81
Days, mythical significance of, 72
De Quincey, T., 64
Development of idea of time, 27 ff.
Distance
  effect on time estimation—see Tau
  effect

interrelation with speed and time, 48, 90
Dostoevski, F.M., 74
Driving, distance, speed and time, estimations, 45, 46, 47, 49
Drugs, effect on time estimation of, 64, 65

E

Einstein, A., 50
Epilepsy, and temporal judgements, 61
Estimation of time
  and age, 36
  effects of emotion, 32, 34, 35, 89
  effects of length of interval, 19, 32
  effects of tedium, 84-85
  effects of temperature, 3, 4, 22, 30, 60
  long intervals, 29
  methods of
    counting, 4
    estimation, 4, 18
    production, 5, 18
    reproduction, 18
    straight line, 31, 37
  past time, 58, 59
  physiological factors, 22, 27
Experimental neurosis, time dependence of, 66

F

Fechner, G. T., 14, 21
Films, time elements in, 74
Fraisse, P., 13, 51, 54
Francois, Marcel, 3, 5
Freud, S., 64
Future
  childrens' idea of, 28, 36
  emotional tension, 34 ff.
  subjective representation of, 37
Futureness, 33

H

Harker, Dr. Janet, 7
Helson, H., 40

Hoagland, H., 4, 5, 83
Hypnosis, and subjective time, 8, 63
Hypothermia, 3

I

Idle-active paradox, 84
Illiad, the, 72
Images of time
  Greek, 76-7, 78
  Iranian, 78
Internal clock, 3 ff., 83 ff.
  discrepancies, 59, 81
  types of, 8, 18

J

Jackson, Hughlings, 61, 88
James, William, 19
Jones, E., 61

K

Kappa-effect, 41-43, 51, 86
  anti-kappa effect, 53
Kappa-movement effect, 45, 49
Korsakov's syndrome, 59

L

Liddell, H.S., 66

M

Mach, E., 13, 14. 16, 51, 58, 90, **91**
Mental illness, and time perception, 59 ff.
Mills, J.N., 8, 12
Mind wandering, 19, 20
Model of psychological time, 83 et seq.
Myth and time, 72 et seq.
  mixing of past present and future, 72-4
  significance of days, 72

N

Nietzsche, F., 33

P

Pacemaker, 83-84, 85, 86, 88
Past
  childrens ideas of, 28
  estimation of, see "Estimation of time"
  subjective representation of, 31
Pavlov, I., 66

Phi-phenomenon, 62
Piaget, J., 50-56
Piéron, Henri, 3, 5, 30
Priestley, J.B., 74
Projector model, 62, 85, 88
Propitious days, 72
Prothetic continua, 21
Proust, M., 33, 74, 82

R

Recall of temporal order, 29
Relativity theory, 50
Religion, time in, 75-76
Richter, C.P., 7, 8
Russell, B., 63

S

Scales of apparent duration, 13-14
Schmidt, H.D., 25, 26
Senile dementia, 59
Shakespeare, W., 81
Siffre, Michel, 30
Simultaneity, 53, 55
Speed
  cues in estimation of, 50
  dependence of child's time estimates
    on, 52
  estimation of, 49
  interrelation with time and distance,
    48, 90
Stevens, S.S., 21, 22
Store, 83-4, 89
Stuttering, 88
Subjective probability
  response delay as an index of, 23
    et seq.
Subjective time, relation with objective,
  31

T

Tau-effect, 41, 51
  anti-tau effect, 46
Tau-movement effect, 41
Temporal agoraphobia, 61
Temporal claustrophobia, 61
Temporal horizon, 34
Temporal order, 29, 58
  confusion between temporal and spa-
    tial order, 51, 65
Tension
  and the future, 34 ff.
  gradient, 35

Time
  accuracy of estimations, 10, 16, 29
  allegorical, 79-81
  calendar, 22, 23, 30, 60, 67, 68
  and children, 52-55, 90
  conditioning to, 35
  cues in estimation, 11
  development of ideas of, 27 ff., 50
  discrimination of order, 16
  effects on estimation of distance: see
    Kappa-effect
  estimation of, see Estimation of time
  filled and unfilled, 14-15
  interrelation with speed and distance,
    48, 90
  levels of adaptation to, 13
  modes of, in novels, 74
  models of, see Models

  the "moment" 17, 62, 63, 86
  psychogenesis of, 50, 91
  relativity of, 40 *et seq.*
  sensory effects, 17, 86-87
  in society, 6, 67-68
  subjective value of, 66, 67, 68, 69
Treisman, M., 83

V

Value of time, 67
Van't Hoff's law, 4
Von Chamisso, A., 34

W

Weber's law, 14, 21, 32
Work, and apparent duration, 53-54